Physics for CCEA A2

Revision Guide

Colourpoint
Educational

Pat Carson and Roy White

© Roy White, Pat Carson and Colourpoint Books 2012

ISBN: 978 1 78073 019 6

First Edition
Second Impression

Layout and design: April Sky Design, Newtownards
Printed by: GPS Colour Graphics Ltd, Belfast

Colourpoint Educational
An imprint of Colourpoint Creative Limited
Colourpoint House
Jubilee Business Park
21 Jubilee Road
Newtownards
County Down
Northern Ireland
BT23 4YH

Tel: 028 9182 6339
Fax: 028 9182 1900
E-mail: info@colourpoint.co.uk
Web site: www.colourpointeducational.com

The Authors

Roy White has been teaching Physics to A-level for over 30 years in Belfast. He is currently Head of Department and an enthusiastic classroom practitioner. In addition to this text, he has been the author or co-author of three successful books supporting the work of science teachers in Northern Ireland.

Pat Carson has been teaching Physics to A level for over 30 years in Belfast and Londonderry. He is currently Vice-Principal in a Londonderry Grammar school.

The authors co-wrote Colourpoint's successful A-level textbooks *Physics for CCEA AS Level* and *Physics for CCEA A2 Level*.

Important Note to Students

This guide has been written to help students preparing for the A2 Physics specification from CCEA. While Colourpoint Books and the authors have taken every care in its production, we are not able to guarantee that the book is completely error-free. Additionally, while the book has been written to closely match the CCEA specification, it the responsibility of each candidate to satisfy themselves that they have fully met the requirements of the CCEA specification prior to sitting an exam set by that body. For this reason, and because specifications change with time, we strongly advise every candidate to avail of a qualified teacher and to check the contents of the most recent specification for themselves prior to the exam. Colourpoint Books therefore cannot be held responsible for any errors or omissions in this book or any consequences thereof.

Copyright of Past Paper Questions

The past paper questions in this book have been reproduced with permission of CCEA. CCEA GCE AS/2 Physics Past Papers – 2009-12. ©CCEA 2012.

Contents

Unit 4 (A2 1)
Momentum, Thermal Physics, Circular Motion, Oscillations, Atomic and Nuclear Physics

4.1 Momentum

Students should be able to:

4.1.1 Define momentum;

4.1.2 Calculate momentum;

4.1.3 Demonstrate an appreciation of the conservation of linear momentum;

4.1.4 Perform calculations involving collisions in one dimension;

4.1.5 Use the terms 'elastic' and 'inelastic' to describe collisions;

Momentum is defined as **the product of mass and velocity**.

In symbols this is often written: $p = mv$

where p = the momentum in Ns (or kg ms^{-1})

m = the mass in kg and

v = the velocity in ms^{-1}

Momentum and velocity are vectors and take place in the same direction.

> ### Worked Example
>
> *Calculate the momentum of a car of mass 800 kg travelling due North with a speed of 15 ms^{-1} and show that the unit Ns is equivalent to the unit kg ms^{-1}.*
>
> $p = mv = 800 \times 15 = 12000$ Ns due North
>
> From $F = ma$, the unit of force, the newton, is equivalent to the unit kg ms^{-2}
>
> So, the unit Ns = kg ms$^{-2} \times$ s = kg ms^{-1}

Principle of Conservation of Linear Momentum

If no external forces are acting, the total momentum of a system of colliding bodies is constant. An alternative phrasing is that in the absence of external forces, the total momentum before a collision is equal to the total momentum after the collision. Since **momentum is a vector** we must assign **one direction as positive and the opposite direction as negative**.

> ### Worked Example
>
> *A toy truck of mass 400 g, moving to the right with a speed of 4 ms^{-1} collides with and sticks to a toy tricycle of mass 1600 g moving to the left with a speed of 3 ms^{-1}. Calculate:*
>
> *(a) the momentum of each toy prior to the collision and*
>
> *(b) the velocity of the combination after the collision*
>
> (a) Taking motion to the right as positive and motion to the left as negative:
>
> Momentum of truck before collision = $mv = 0.4$ kg $\times +4$ ms$^{-1} = +1.6$ kg ms^{-1}
>
> Momentum of tricycle before collision = $mv = 1.6$ kg $\times -3$ ms$^{-1} = -4.8$ kg ms^{-1}
>
> (b) total momentum before collision = total momentum after the collision. So:
>
> {$1.6 + (-4.8)$} = mass of combination $\times$ velocity of combination after collision
>
> $-3.2 = (0.4 + 1.6) \times v_{after}$
>
> $v_{after} = -3.2 \div 2.0 = -1.6$ ms^{-1}
>
> The minus sign shows that the **combined truck and tricycle is moving to the left**, that is, it is moving in the same direction as the tricycle was moving originally.

Collision Classification

Collisions may be classified as elastic or inelastic.

- **Elastic** collisions are those in which **kinetic energy is conserved**. These only occur on an atomic scale, such as the collision of two molecules of an ideal gas.
- **Inelastic** collisions are those in which **kinetic energy is not conserved.** An example is the collision of a tennis ball with a racquet.

A **completely inelastic** collision is one in which two bodies stick together on impact. Here the loss of kinetic energy is very large, though not complete. An example is a rifle bullet embedding itself in a sandbag.

The **Law of Conservation of Energy** tells us that energy cannot be created or destroyed but it can change from one form into another. For example, some of the kinetic energy of a bullet hitting a sandbag will be converted into heat and sound.

We can sum up these ideas in a table:

	Momentum	Kinetic energy	Total energy
Inelastic Collisions	is conserved	is NOT conserved	is conserved
Elastic Collisions	is conserved	is conserved	is conserved

Exercise 1

1. A trolley of mass 0.8 kg has a velocity 0.4 ms⁻¹ to the right. It collides head on and sticks to another trolley of mass 0.6 kg which is moving with a velocity 0.3 ms⁻¹ in the opposite direction as illustrated in the diagram. During the collision some energy is converted into heat and sound.

(i) Calculate the magnitude and direction of the velocity of the trolleys after the collision.

(ii) Is this an example of an elastic or an inelastic collision? Explain your answer.

(CCEA AY211 Summer 2011)

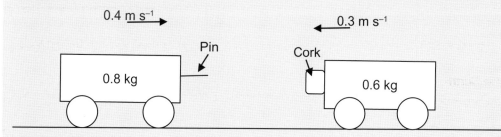

4.2 Thermal Physics

Students should be able to:

4.2.1 Describe simple experiments on the behaviour of gases to show that pV = constant for a fixed mass of gas at constant temperature, and $\frac{p}{T}$ = **constant** for a fixed mass of gas at constant volume, leading to the equation $\frac{pV}{T}$ = constant;

4.2.2 Recall and use the ideal gas equation pV = nRT;

4.2.3 Recall and use the ideal gas equation in the form pV = NkT;

4.2.4 Use the equation $pV = \frac{1}{3}Nm\langle c^2 \rangle$;

4.2.5 Demonstrate an understanding of the concept of absolute zero of temperature;

4.2.6 Demonstrate an understanding of the concept of internal energy as the random distribution of potential and kinetic energy among molecules;

4.2.7 Use the equations for average molecular kinetic energy $\frac{1}{2}m\langle c^2 \rangle = \frac{3kT}{2}$

4.2.8 Perform and describe an electrical method for determination of specific heat capacity;

4.2.9 Use the equation Q = mcΔθ

The Behaviour of Gases

On a macroscopic scale the behaviour of gases is described by three laws – **Boyle's Law**, **Charles' Law** and the **Pressure Law**. You **need to be able to describe simple experiments which show Boyle's Law and the Pressure Law** (but **not** Charles' Law).

Boyle's Law

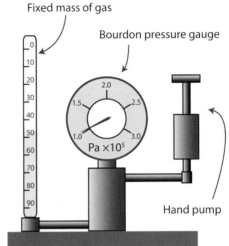

Fixed mass of gas

Bourdon pressure gauge

Hand pump

- In the diagram on the right, the oil in the closed tube traps a **fixed mass** of air above it. The **length of the air column is proportional to its volume**. The experiment involves measuring the length of this column and recording the corresponding pressure on the Bourdon gauge.
- Using the hand pump (or foot pump) we can very slowly increase the pressure acting on the trapped air.
- Compressing the gas warms it slightly, so after every compression we need to wait a few moments for the temperature of the trapped air to return to room temperature.
- We can repeat this for several more values of pressure and record the new length (volume) and pressure readings in a table.

The first graph is of pressure against volume. It is a curve which shows that volume decreases as pressure increases.

To determine the nature of this inverse relationship, we plot a graph of volume against 1/pressure as shown in the second graph. This graph is a straight line through the origin, confirming **Boyle's Law**:

For a fixed mass of gas at constant temperature, the volume is inversely proportional to the applied pressure.

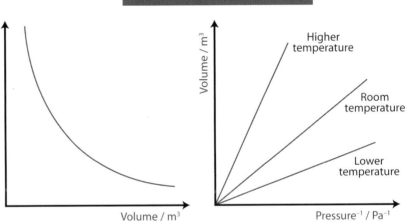

Boyle's Law can be expressed as an equation:

pressure × volume = constant   or   PV = a constant

The Pressure Law (sometimes called Gay Lussac's law)

This experiment involves investigating how the pressure of a fixed mass of air at constant volume varies as the temperature changes. Using the apparatus opposite, the pressure is measured using a Bourdon pressure gauge.

- The bulb of a large glass flask is totally immersed in a tall beaker of cold water with a thermometer.
- Throughout the experiment the water is stirred regularly.
- The pressure of the trapped air and the temperature are then recorded in a table.
- The water is then heated until it is about 10°C hotter and another pair of readings of pressure and temperature are recorded.
- This process is repeated, increasing the temperature of the water until it boils.
- A graph is then plotted of pressure against temperature in degrees Celsius, as shown on the next page.

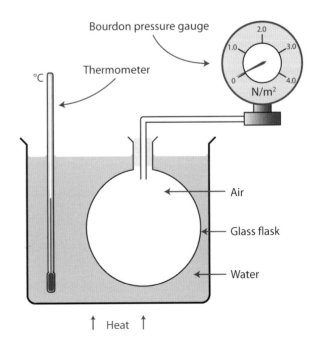

Bourdon pressure gauge

Thermometer

Air

Glass flask

Water

↑ Heat ↑

The graph of pressure against the **Celsius** temperature is a straight line of positive slope. However as the graph does not pass through the origin, it does not illustrate proportionality.

In AS 1 you were introduced to the Kelvin scale, given by:

T = θ + 273 where:

T is the temperature in Kelvin and

θ is the temperature in degrees Celsius

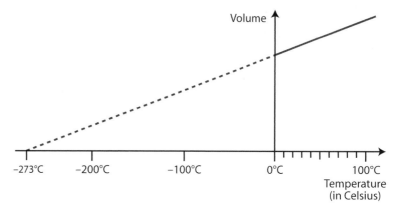

The temperature 0 Kelvin is called the **absolute zero** of temperature. Absolute zero is the temperature at which **all molecular motion stops** and is approximately −273.16°C, although for purposes of calculations, it is sufficient to use −273°C. There is no temperature below 0 Kelvin.

The graph of pressure against Kelvin temperature is a straight line passing through the origin, confirming the **Pressure Law**:

For a fixed mass of gas, at constant volume, the pressure is directly proportional to the Kelvin temperature.

The Pressure Law can be expressed as an equation:

$$p = \text{constant} \times T \quad \text{or} \quad \frac{p}{T} = \text{constant}$$

where:

p = the pressure of the gas and

T = the temperature in Kelvin

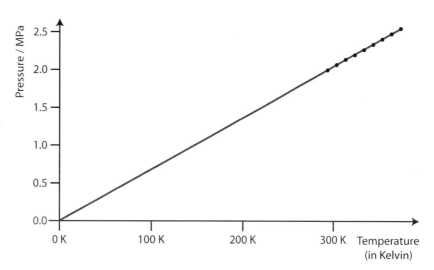

Charles' Law

While you need not learn the experiment which demonstrates Charles' Law, you must know the statement of the law and how to apply it:

For a fixed mass of gas at constant pressure, the volume is directly proportional to the Kelvin temperature.

Charles' Law can be expressed as an equation:

$$V = \text{constant} \times T \quad \text{or} \quad \frac{V}{T} = \text{constant}$$

where:

V = the gas volume and

T = the temperature in Kelvin

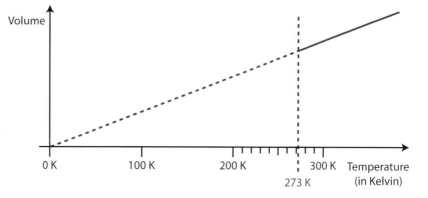

The equations for Boyle's Law, Charles' Law and the Pressure Law can be combined into one, called the **ideal gas equation**:

$$\frac{pV}{T} = \text{a constant}$$

If a fixed mass of gas has values p_1, V_1 and T_1, and then some time later has values p_2, V_2 and T_2, then the equation becomes:

$$\frac{p_1 V_1}{T_1} = \frac{p_2 V_2}{T_2}$$

Exercise 2

1. (i) A student gives the following incomplete statement of one of the laws for an ideal gas:

   "The volume of an ideal gas is inversely proportional to the pressure applied to it."

   Identify two important omissions from the correct and complete version of this statement.

   (ii) Describe an experiment to investigate the law referred to in (i). Include a labelled diagram. Indicate how you would process your results to clearly demonstrate the relationship between pressure and volume.

2. The air pressure inside a car tyre is 280 kPa at a temperature of 15°C. After a journey the pressure rises to 310 kPa. Assuming the volume of air remains constant, calculate the new temperature of the air in the tyre.

   (CCEA AY211 Summer 2011, modified)

The Mole

The experimental gas laws show that for a **fixed mass** of gas: **pV = a constant × T**

The constant depends only on the number of molecules in the gas. The best way to express this is in terms of the number of **moles** of gas. **Amount of substance** is measured in moles and the mole (abbreviated to **mol**) is one of the six SI base units introduced in your AS course. But what exactly is a mole?

The mole is the amount of substance which contains as many particles as there are atoms in 0.012 kg of carbon–12. So, a mole of gas molecules is simply Avogadro's number of those molecules; a mole of electrons is Avogadro's number of electrons and so on. **Avogadro's number is the number of particles per mole.** Its numerical value is 6.02×10^{23} mol^{-1}.

Kinetic Theory and Ideal Gases

The **kinetic theory** attempts to explain the properties of a gas by studying the behaviour of the molecules. To apply the kinetic theory we have to make some assumptions. These assumptions define the characteristics of what physicists call **an ideal gas**. The Ideal Gas Assumptions are:

- There are no intermolecular forces – the only time the molecules exert a force on each other is when they collide.
- The molecules themselves have negligible volume compared to the volume of the gas.
- The collisions between molecules and between molecules and the walls of the container are elastic, so both kinetic energy and momentum are conserved.
- The duration of a collision is negligible compared with the time between collisions.
- Between collisions the molecules move with constant velocity.

Kinetic Theory & Gas Properties

1. How does the kinetic theory explain the pressure exerted by a gas on the walls of the container?	**2. Boyle's Law tells us that when the volume of a fixed mass of gas at constant temperature is doubled the pressure halves. How does the kinetic theory explain this?**
• Molecules collide elastically with the walls, so each collision results in a momentum change for the molecules. • A momentum change implies a force was exerted on the molecules by the wall and of course by the molecule on the wall. • The total force on the wall is the sum of the forces exerted by all the colliding molecules. • The pressure on the wall is ratio of this total force to the area of the wall.	• Doubling the volume means that the molecules have on average twice as far to travel to the walls of the container. • The momentum change per collision is the same. • So the force caused by each collision is the same. • But the greater distance means that only half as many collisions occur per second. • So the pressure halves.
3. The Pressure Law tells us that as the temperature a fixed mass of gas at constant volume is increased the pressure increases. How does the kinetic theory explain this?	**4. Charles' Law tells us that as the temperature of a fixed mass of gas at constant pressure is increased the volume increases. How does the kinetic theory explain this?**
• Increasing temperature increases the speed and momentum of the molecules. • The momentum change per collision increases and so also does the number of collision per second. • Both of these contribute to an increase in pressure.	• Increasing temperature increases the momentum of the molecules and the collision frequency with the walls. • To maintain the same pressure the number of collisions per second must decrease. • Expansion makes the molecules travel a greater distance before they collide with the container. • A greater distance means a greater time and so the number of collisions per second is reduced to keep the pressure remains constant.

The Universal Gas Constant, R

We can now write down the equation for **an ideal gas:**   **pV = nRT** where:

p = the gas pressure in Pa
V = the gas volume in m³
n = the number of moles of gas
T = the temperature of gas in Kelvin
R = a constant, known as the **universal gas constant**

R has a value of 8.31 J mol⁻¹ K⁻¹ and is a **universal** constant because **it applies to all gases**, provided their behaviour is ideal.
This equation is not supplied in the CCEA formula sheet and must be remembered.

Exercise 3

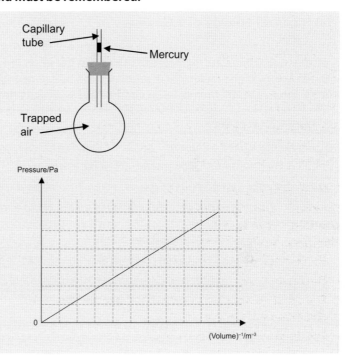

1. A flask contains air at a temperature of 17 °C and is
   sealed with a rubber bung. A capillary tube of diameter
   3.0 mm containing a short column of mercury is inserted
   into the bung. The volume of air trapped is 40 cm³. The
   arrangement is shown opposite.

   The flask is warmed gently. Calculate the temperature
   reached when the mercury column moves 120 mm up
   the capillary tube if the pressure remains at atmospheric
   level throughout.

   (CCEA AY211 January 2011, modified)

2. The results from a Boyles' Law experiment are displayed
   in the graph opposite.

   For a set of results the gradient is measured and found to
   be 12 200 Pa m³.

   Show that the temperature of the gas is 4°C if the gas
   contains 5.30 moles.

   (CCEA AY211 Summer 2010, modified)

The Boltzmann Constant

The Boltzmann constant, k, is defined by the equation: $\mathbf{k = \dfrac{R}{N_A}}$

where   R = the universal gas constant
        N_A = Avogadro's number

The Boltzmann constant is therefore:

8.31 J mol⁻¹ K⁻¹ ÷ 6.02×10^{23} mol⁻¹ and has a value of 1.38×10^{-23} JK⁻¹.

Combining the definitions of the Boltzmann constant and Avogadro's Number with the ideal gas equation gives the
equation: **pV = NkT**

This equation is important because it links the number of particles in the gas, N, with its macroscopic properties of pressure
volume and temperature. **This equation is not supplied in the CCEA formula sheet and must be remembered.**

Linking the Equation of State to the Molecular Speeds of Gases

If the speeds of the N molecules in a sample of gas are $c_1, c_2, c_3, ..., c_N$, then:

The **mean speed**, $\langle c \rangle$ is defined by: $\langle c \rangle = \dfrac{c_1 + c_2 + c_3 + ...c_N}{N}$

The **mean square speed** is defined by: $\langle c^2 \rangle = \dfrac{c_1{}^2 + c_2{}^2 + c_3{}^2 + ...c_N{}^2}{N}$

The **root mean square speed** is defined by: $c_{rms} = \dfrac{\sqrt{\langle c^2 \rangle}}{N}$

There is a **statistical relationship** between the pressure, volume, mass and speed of the molecules. $\mathbf{pV = \dfrac{1}{3} Nm \langle c^2 \rangle}$

CCEA students do not have to derive this equation although some texts show where it comes from in great detail. This
equation is given in the CCEA formula sheet.

Molecular Speeds and Temperature

Since $pV = \frac{1}{3}Nm\langle c^2 \rangle$ and $pV = NkT$ we can write $\frac{1}{3}Nm\langle c^2 \rangle = NkT$

Multiplying both sides by $\frac{3}{2N}$ gives: $\frac{1}{2}m\langle c^2 \rangle = \frac{3kT}{2}$

This equation links the average kinetic energy of a collection of gas molecules with the Kelvin temperature.

The Internal Energy of a Gas

The internal energy of a **real** gas is the sum of the potential and kinetic energy of its molecules. However, for **ideal** gases it is assumed that there are **no forces of attraction between the atoms**. So, **ideal gases possess no potential energy**. The internal energy of the molecules of an ideal gas is therefore **entirely kinetic**. The above equation shows that the **average kinetic energy of the molecules in an ideal gas is directly proportional to the Kelvin temperature.**

Worked Example

A cylinder has a fixed volume of 1.36×10^{-3} m³ and contains a gas at a pressure of 1.04×10^5 Pa when the temperature is 15°C.

(i) Calculate the number of gas molecules in the container.

(ii) Calculate the new pressure of the gas when the temperature is increased to 25°C.

(iii) Calculate the increase in kinetic energy of all the gas molecules in the container caused when the temperature is increased to 25°C.

(i) $PV = NkT$ so, $N = \dfrac{PV}{kT} = \dfrac{1.04 \times 10^5 \times 1.36 \times 10^{-3}}{1.38 \times 10^{-23} \times 288} = 3.56 \times 10^{22}$ molecules

(ii) From the Pressure Law, $P_2 = \dfrac{P_1 \times T_2}{T_1} = \dfrac{1.04 \times 10^5 \times 298}{288} = 1.08 \times 10^5$ Pa

(iii) Average KE of a molecule $= \dfrac{3}{2}kT$, so

Increase in KE $= \dfrac{3}{2}Nk(T_2 - T_1) = \dfrac{3}{2} \times 3.56 \times 10^{22} \times 1.38 \times 10^{-23} \times (288 - 278) = 7.37$ J

Worked Example

A tyre contains a gas at a pressure of 150 kPa. If the gas has a density of 2.0 kg m⁻³, find the root mean square speed of the molecules.

Since $PV = \frac{1}{3}Nm\langle c^2 \rangle$ therefore $P = \frac{1}{3}Nm\langle c^2 \rangle \div V$

$$P = \frac{1}{3} \times \frac{\text{mass of gas}}{\text{volume}} \times \langle c^2 \rangle = \frac{1}{3} \times \text{density} \times \langle c^2 \rangle$$

So, $\langle c^2 \rangle = \dfrac{3P}{\text{density}} = \dfrac{3 \times 150 \times 10^3}{2} = 2.25 \times 10^5$

So $c_{rms} = 474$ ms⁻¹

Specific Heat Capacity (SHC)

The specific heat capacity, c, of a material is the quantity of heat energy needed to raise the temperature of 1 kg of the material by 1 Kelvin. The units of specific heat capacity are **J kg⁻¹ K⁻¹ (or J kg⁻¹ °C⁻¹).**

This definition leads to the equation: **$Q = mc\Delta\theta$** where

where   Q = quantity of heat energy supplied, in J

      m = mass of the object, in kg

      c = the SHC of the material in J kg⁻¹ K⁻¹

      $\Delta\theta$ = the change in temperature in Kelvin

Experiment to Measure Specific Heat Capacity of a Metal

A metal cylinder has two holes in it, one to hold an electrical heater and other to hold a thermometer. A small amount of oil in the hole containing the thermometer is used to **improve the thermal contact** between the thermometer and the metal.

The mass, m, of the metal cylinder is measured using a balance and the **initial temperature, T_1**, of the metal is measured with a thermometer. The amount of energy can be found using a voltmeter, ammeter and stop clock.

The **power** of the heater = current × voltage = $I \times V$

The stop clock is used to determine the time, t, the heater is switched on.

Energy supplied, $Q = I \times V \times t$

The final temperature is taken as the **highest temperature, T_2**, reached by the block **after the heater is switched off**. The temperature rise, $\Delta\theta$, is therefore $T_2 - T_1$ and the SHC is calculated as $Q \div m\Delta\theta$.
A similar method is used to find the specific heat capacity of a liquid.

Refinements

- The experimental value for SHC is generally larger than the true value because heat is lost from the material under test. To reduce heat loss the metal lock or calorimeter is generally wrapped in an insulator, such as expanded polystyrene.
- Another technique is to cool the metal to a temperature of around 5°C less than room temperature. Heating continues until the metal or liquid temperature is about 5°C **above** room temperature. During the time when the material is below room temperature heat is absorbed from the environment. When the material is above room temperature, heat is lost to the environment. By doing this it is hoped that the heat lost to the environment cancels the heat gained from the environment, and results in a value for the specific heat capacity closer to that which is generally accepted.
- The worked example below shows how allowance can also be made for the heat lost to the calorimeter in an experiment to find the SHC of a liquid.

Worked Example

In an experiment, 240 g of milk is heated from room temperature in a container of mass 75.0 g made from copper of specific heat capacity of 390 J kg^{-1} °C^{-1}. A small electrical heater is placed in the milk. The potential difference across the heater is 12.0 V, the current through it is 2.60 A and the heater remains on for 6 minutes and 50 s. During this time, the temperature of the container and its contents increases by 13 °C above room temperature. Calculate

(i) the total heat supplied by the heater,

(ii) the heat absorbed by the copper, and

(iii) the specific heat capacity of the milk.

CCEA AY211 January 2010 (modified)

(i) Heat = power × time = $(IV) \times t = 2.60 \times 12 \times 410 = 12792$ J ≈ 12800 J

(ii) $Q = mc\Delta\theta = 0.075 \times 390 \times 13 = 380.25$ J ≈ 380 J

(iii) Heat absorbed by milk = 12792 − 380.25 = 12411.75 J

$$c = \frac{Q}{m\Delta\theta} = \frac{12411.75}{0.24 \times 13} = 3978.125 \approx 3980 \text{ Jkg}^{-1} \text{ K}^{-1}$$

4.3 Uniform Circular Motion

Students should be able to:

4.3.1 Demonstrate an understanding of the concept of angular velocity;

4.3.2 Recall and use the equation $v = r\omega$;

4.3.3 Apply the relationship $F = ma = \dfrac{mv^2}{r}$ to motion in a circle at constant speed;

Basic Ideas

Suppose an object is moving at a steady speed, v, in a circle of radius, r. Suppose the radius vector sweeps through an angle θ radians, in a time t seconds, as the object moves through arc length s from point P to P'. Then we can define:

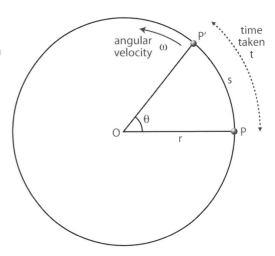

Arc length, s, is related to the angle θ by the definition of the radian. This relationship is

$s = r\theta$

where s and r have the same units for length and θ is in radians

Angular velocity, ω, is defined as the angle swept out by the radius vector in one second. So by definition:

$$\omega = \frac{\theta}{t}$$

and ω is measured in radians per second.

Since speed, v, is the rate of change of distance with time, then combining equations in the boxes above enables us to write:

$$v = \frac{s}{t} = \frac{r\theta}{t} = r\omega$$

The **periodic time** of the motion, **T**, is defined as the time taken for the particle to travel once round the circle through 2π radians. So by definition:

$$T = \frac{s}{v} = \frac{2\pi r}{r\omega} = \frac{2\pi}{\omega}$$

The **frequency, f,** of the motion is the number of revolutions made per second. Since the particle takes T seconds to make one revolution, we can write:

$$f = \frac{1}{T} = \frac{\omega}{2\pi}$$

Centripetal Acceleration

Any particle moving in a circular path at a constant speed must be accelerating because the direction of its motion, and hence its velocity, is constantly changing. **This acceleration is always directed towards the centre of the circle and is called centripetal acceleration.** The magnitude of the centripetal acceleration is denoted by the symbol **a** and is given by:

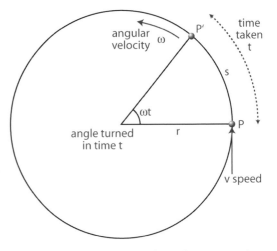

$$a = v\omega = r\omega^2 = \frac{v^2}{r}$$

Since the orbiting particle is being accelerated there must also be an accelerating force in accordance with Newton's Second Law. This force, **F**, is given by the equation:

$$F = ma = mv\omega = mr\omega^2 = \frac{mv^2}{r}$$

The CCEA specification requires candidates to recall and be able to use of the equations for centripetal acceleration and centripetal force, but not how to derive them.

Causes of the Centripetal Force

Note that the **circular motion does not produce the force.** Rather, **the force is needed for circular motion to take place.** Without this force the object would travel in a straight line along the tangent to the curve. The table below identifies the cause of the centripetal force in four different situations.

Physical Situation	Cause of Centripetal Force
A planet orbiting the Sun	**Gravitational force** between the Sun and the planet
Electrons orbiting the nucleus of an atom	**Electrical force** between the positively charged nucleus and the negatively charged electron
A "conker" whirled in a circle at the end of a string	The **tension** in the string
A racing car going round a circular track	The **friction force** between the tyres and the track

Worked Example

(a) *The radius of the Earth at the equator is 6.38×10⁶ m. The Earth rotates with a period of 24.0 hours. Calculate:*
  (i) the angular velocity of a point on the equator.
  (ii) the linear velocity at a point on the equator.

(b) *Gravity provides a pull on the student towards the centre of the Earth. The magnitude of this force is 728 N. The student measures his weight when at the equator. Will the value obtained be 728 N or more or less than 728 N? Explain your answer.*

CCEA AY211 Summer 2011 (modified)

(a) (i) Using $\omega = \dfrac{2\pi}{T}$ so $T = \dfrac{2\pi}{\omega} = \dfrac{2\pi}{24 \times 3600} = 7.27\times10^{-5}$ rad s^{-1}

(ii) Using $v = r\omega = 6.38\times10^{6} \times 7.27\times10^{-5} = 464$ ms^{-1}

(b) First calculate $m = \dfrac{F}{a} = \dfrac{728}{9.81} = 74.21$ kg

Using $F = \dfrac{mv^2}{r} = \dfrac{74.21 \times 464^2}{6.38\times10^{6}} = 2.50$ N

So the force at equator = 728 − 2.50 = 725.5 N

This is less than 728 N, because some of the gravitational force is used to provide the centripetal force.

Exercise 4

1. A motorcyclist goes round a bend in a horizontal road at a constant speed of 40 km hr⁻¹. The radius of curvature of the bend is 12.0 m.

(a) (i) Explain why this motorcyclist has an angular velocity.

  (ii) Calculate the value of the angular velocity, ω, of the motorcyclist as he rounds the bend.

(b) (i) Explain why a force is needed if the motorcyclist is to get round the bend.

  (ii) State how this force is produced.

(c) The motorcyclist has a mass of 90 kg and the motorcycle has a mass of 260 kg.

  Calculate the magnitude of the force needed to go round the bend at 40 km hr⁻¹.

(CCEA AY211 January 2011, modified)

Motion in a Vertical Circle

The diagram opposite shows an object of mass m being whirled clockwise at a constant speed v in a vertical circle at the end of a piece of string of length L. The resultant force on the object is not constant.

At point A, the tension T₁ in the string is given by:

$$T_1 + mg = \frac{mv^2}{L} \quad \text{so:} \quad \mathbf{T_1 = \frac{mv^2}{L} - mg}$$

At point C, the tension T₂ in the string is given by:

$$T_2 - mg = \frac{mv^2}{L} \quad \text{so:} \quad \mathbf{T_2 = \frac{mv^2}{L} + mg}$$

At points B and D the tension alone provides the centripetal force, so:

$$\mathbf{T = \frac{mv^2}{L}}$$

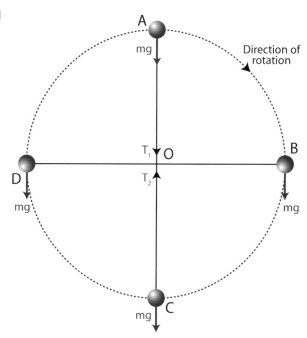

Circling at an Angle

The diagram shows a conical pendulum. The vertical component tension in the string (T sinθ), balances the weight of the orbiting mass. The horizontal component of the tension provides the centripetal force. So,

$$T \sin\theta = mg \text{ and } T \cos\theta = \frac{mv^2}{R}$$

Dividing one equation by the other gives:

$$\frac{T \sin\theta}{T \cos\theta} = \tan\theta = mg \div \frac{mv^2}{R} = \frac{Rg}{v^2}$$

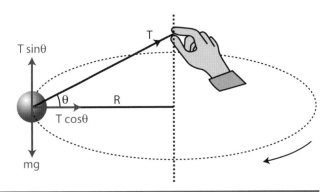

4.4 Simple Harmonic Motion

Students should be able to:

4.4.1 Define simple harmonic motion using the equation $a = -\omega^2 x$ where $\omega = 2\pi f$;

4.4.2 Perform calculations using $x = A \cos \omega t$;

4.4.3 Demonstrate an understanding of s.h.m. graphs to include measuring velocity from the gradient of a displacement time graph;

4.4.4 Know and be able to use the terms free vibrations, forced vibrations, resonance and damping in this context;

4.4.5 Understand the concepts of light damping, overdamping and critical damping;

4.4.6 Describe mechanical examples of resonance and damping;

Definition: A particle moves with **Simple Harmonic Motion (SHM)** if its acceleration is proportional to its displacement from a fixed point and the direction of the acceleration is always towards that fixed point.

The definition of SHM gives rise to the equation

$$a = -\omega^2 x$$

where   a = the acceleration in ms^{-2}

ω^2 = a constant in s^{-2}

x = the distance from the fixed point in m

The minus indicates that the acceleration and displacement are in opposite directions. The graphs below illustrate the relationships between acceleration, force and displacement. The amplitude, or maximum displacement, of the motion is denoted by the letter A.

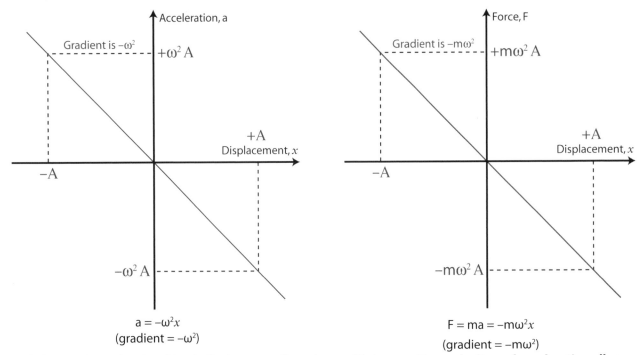

In simple harmonic motion the object's **displacement** from the equilibrium position, **velocity and acceleration all vary with time**. It is not necessary to be able to derive the equations that apply to each of these physical quantities, but it is necessary to be able to use them.

In the diagram below the object R moves along the line YX with simple harmonic motion. The centre of oscillation is the point O. **At time t = 0 the object is at Y and moving towards O.**

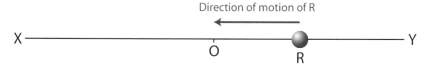

The graphs show how the displacement x, (represented by the vector OR) and the velocity v of the object vary with time t. The time to complete one oscillation (YOXOY) is the period T.

The **displacement** x varies sinusoidally with time, t. Its value at any instant is given by:

$x = A \cos \omega t$

where   A is equal to OY, the amplitude of the oscillation
        ω = the angular frequency in radians per second.

Note that given the displacement–time graph, we can obtain the velocity at any instant by drawing the appropriate tangent at that point and finding the gradient.

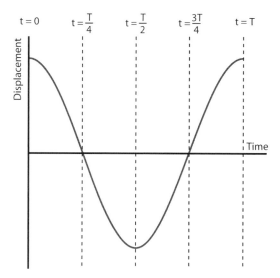

The **velocity** at any instant is equal to the gradient of the displacement–time graph at that instant. While the general equation for v is not required by the CCEA specification, it turns out to be:

$v = -\omega A \sin \omega t$

The velocity has a maximum value of ωA at the instant the object passes through the centre of the oscillation.

The minus sign shows that shortly after t = 0 the object is moving in the negative direction (from right to left).

Note that there is a phase difference between the velocity and the displacement. The velocity is at its peak at time $\dfrac{3T}{4}$ and the displacement reaches its peak at time T. We therefore say that the velocity is leading the displacement by a quarter of a period, $\dfrac{T}{4}$, or $\dfrac{\pi}{2}$ radians.

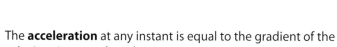

The **acceleration** at any instant is equal to the gradient of the velocity–time graph at that instant.

$a = -\omega^2 A \cos \omega t$

The acceleration has a maximum value of $-\omega^2 A \cos \omega t$ at the instant the object reaches the extremities of its oscillation. The acceleration is zero when the object reaches the centre of the oscillation.

The minus sign tells us that the acceleration is always in the opposite direction to the displacement from O.

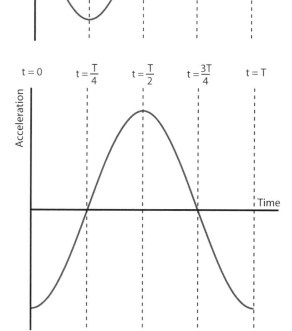

Velocity and Displacement

The defining equation for SHM ($a = -\omega^2 x$) tells us how the acceleration varies with displacement. But how does the velocity vary with displacement? It turns out that:

$$v = \pm\omega\sqrt{(A^2 - x^2)}$$

The ± indicates that the velocity can be positive or negative i.e. to left or to the right or up or down. In other words it refers to direction. The equation above is **not** required by the specification, but it is so useful that it is reproduced here for the sake of completeness.

Summary of Equations for Displacement, Velocity and Acceleration

	Displacement	Velocity	Acceleration
Variation with time	$x = A\cos\omega t$	$v = -\omega A \sin\omega t$	$a = -\omega^2 A \cos\omega t$
Maximum value	Amplitude = A	At fixed point, Max velocity = $\pm\,\omega A$	At extreme displacement, maximum acceleration = $\omega^2 A$
Minimum value	At fixed point, displacement = o	At extreme displacement, minimum velocity = 0	At fixed point, acceleration = o
Variation with displacement		$v = \pm\omega\sqrt{(A^2 - x^2)}$	$a = -\omega^2 x$

The following equation, first seen when looking at circular motion is also applicable to SHM.

Angular frequency: $\omega = 2\pi f = \dfrac{2\pi}{T}$

Worked Example

The graph shows how the displacement of a nitrogen molecule varies with time in the air as a result of a sound wave passing. The molecule can be assumed to execute simple harmonic motion.

(a) Describe the displacement of the nitrogen molecule during the 600 μs duration as shown on the graph.

(b) Using the graph to show that the maximum velocity of the nitrogen molecule is approximately 3 ms⁻¹.

CCEA AY211 Summer 2010 (modified)

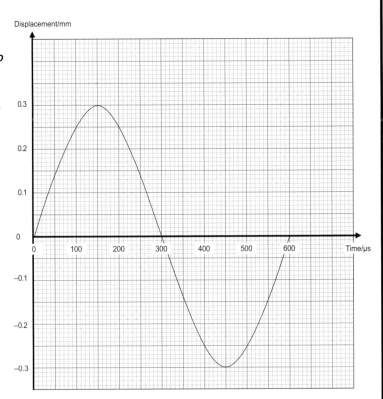

(a) From a fixed point the particle is displaced to one side, then it returns to its initial position in 300 μs; it is then displaced to the opposite side of the fixed point and returns to its initial position after a total time of 600 μs.

(b) Using $\omega = \dfrac{2\pi}{T} = \dfrac{2\pi}{600\times10^{-6}} = \dfrac{10\,000\pi}{3}$ radians per second

So $v_{max} = \omega A = \dfrac{10\,000\pi \times 0.3\times10^{-3}}{3}$ ms⁻¹ $= \pi$ ms⁻¹ ≈ 3 ms⁻¹

Worked Example

A mass executing simple harmonic motion starts at the extreme limit of positive displacement at time **t** = 0, *the magnitude of this displacement is 0.060 m. The mass executes 100 oscillations in 20.0 s.*

(i) Use these data to obtain values for A and ω in the equation $x = A \cos \omega t$.

(ii) Calculate the distance and position of the mass relative to the centre of the motion, 0.13 s after the start of the oscillation. State the direction in which the mass is moving at this time.

(iii) Calculate the maximum speed of this mass.

CCEA AY211 January 2010 (modified)

(i) $A = 0.060$ m and $\omega = \dfrac{2\pi}{T} = \dfrac{2\pi}{0.2} = 10\pi \approx 31.4$ radians per second

(ii) Distance: $x = A \cos \omega t = 0.06 \cos (31.4 \times 0.13) = -0.035$ m

Position: The minus sign shows that the object is on **opposite** side of central position compared to start position.

Direction: The period is 0.2 s, so from time 0.0 s to 0.1 s the mass is moving from the extreme limit of positive displacement towards the extreme limit of negative displacement. From time 0.10 s to 0.15 s (and hence at 0.13 s) the mass is moving **from the extreme limit of negative displacement towards the fixed point of the motion**.

(iii) $v_{max} = \omega A = 10\pi \times 0.060 = 1.88$ ms^{-1}

Free and Damped Oscillations

If a pendulum is set oscillating the amplitude of the oscillation gradually decreases. Eventually it stops oscillating due to the resistive forces of the air and friction between the string and the suspension point. Gradually the pendulum's energy is transferred to heat and sound.

Resistive forces that act on an oscillating system are known as damping forces.
Free oscillations are those which are not damped, such as the vibration of atoms in a metal.

Undamped oscillations are said to be **free oscillations** (i.e. perfect SHM). The displacement varies periodically as shown. However the amplitude remains constant with time.

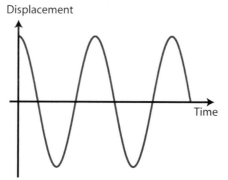

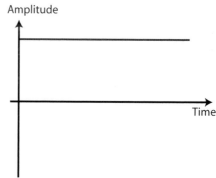

When the system is **lightly damped** the displacement will vary with time as with free oscillations. However the amplitude of the oscillation will gradually get smaller and eventually the oscillations will cease.

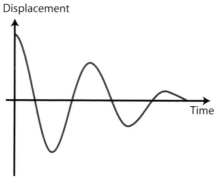

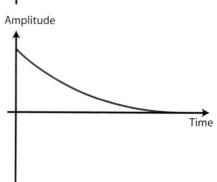

When a system is **heavily damped** no oscillations occur. The system returns very slowly to its equilibrium position.

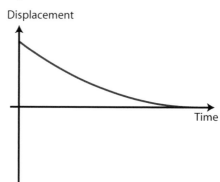

When we have **critical** damping the system returns to its equilibrium position in the shortest possible time, $\frac{T}{4}$ where T is the periodic time.

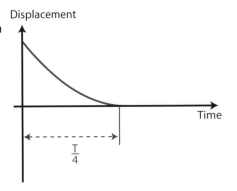

Forced Oscillations and Resonance

A **forced oscillation** is when any external force which varies with time is used to make an object oscillate. For example pushing a child on a swing, or using your hand to make a mass on a spring oscillate by moving your hand up and down.

Forced oscillations can be demonstrated using **Barton's pendulums** (shown opposite). The 'driver' pendulum X has a heavy bob, while the others are paper cones. The driver pendulum is pulled to one side and released. After a time all the pendulums oscillate with very nearly the same frequency as the driver but with different amplitudes. **The paper cone pendulum, A, which has the same length, L, (and hence the same natural frequency) as the driver has the largest amplitude. This is due to resonance.**

Resonance occurs when the frequency of the driving force is the same as the natural frequency of the oscillating system. Any oscillating mechanical system can be made to resonate. Examples include:

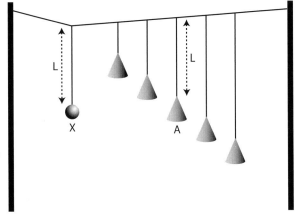

• the air column in a resonance tube

• an oscillating loaded spiral spring

• the vibrating string of a musical instrument.

We recognise resonance when the driven system has maximum amplitude. The graph shows how the amplitude of a forced oscillation depends on the frequency of the force causing it to vibrate (driver frequency). For an undamped or lightly damped system, the amplitude reaches a maximum when the frequency of the driving force equals that of the natural frequency of the oscillating system.

When the damping force is small (light damping) the peak is sharp. However when the damping forces is greater (heavy damping) the **peak is broader** and in fact the maximum occurs **at a slightly lower frequency**. If the damping force is very great the system will not oscillate, so resonance cannot occur.

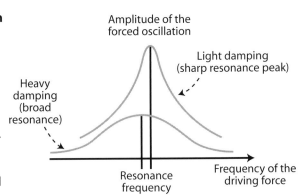

Exercise 5

1. The diagram illustrates an experimental arrangement to investigate resonance and damping. The apparatus consists of a piece of string, initially horizontal, securely fixed at one end, placed over a pulley in order to support a vertical spring to which a mass is attached. A pointer, secured to the lower end of the spring, indicates a position on a vertical metre rule. An oval shaped cam rotates and as it does so it causes the string it comes into contact with to lift twice in each rotation. The rotation frequency of the cam can be altered using a signal generator. This apparatus is used to demonstrate resonance.

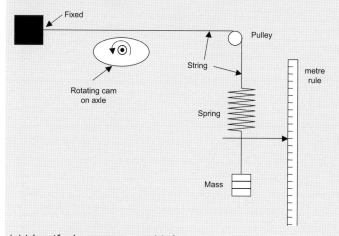

(a) Identify the component(s) that
  (i) is/are forced to vibrate
  (ii) provide(s) the driving force that results in the vibration

(b) (i) Label the vertical axis below and sketch the shape of a typical resonance graph for the system as the frequency of the cam is progressively increased.

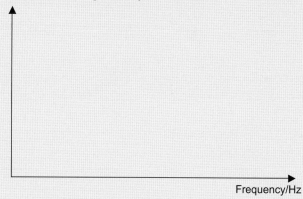

Frequency/Hz

(ii) Suggest a practical method of increasing the damping in the experimental arrangement.
(iii) Sketch the resonance graph expected for the more heavily damped system. Clearly label this new graph D.

(c) Resonance occurs when the signal generator frequency is 16 Hz. That is, the oval shaped cam makes 16 complete rotations every second. What is the natural frequency of the system which has been forced to vibrate?

(CCEA AY211 Summer 2010, modified)

4.5 The Nucleus

4.5.1 Be able to describe evidence for the existence of atomic nuclei, to include alpha particle scattering;

4.5.2 Know and interpret the variation of nuclear radius with nucleon number; and

4.5.3 Use the equation $r = r_0 A^{1/3}$ to estimate the density of nuclear matter.

In 1903 Sir J. J. Thomson developed his "Plum Pudding Model" in which the atom was regarded as a positively charged sphere in which the negatively charged electrons were distributed like currants in a bun in sufficient numbers to make the atom as a whole electrically neutral.

In 1906 Ernest Rutherford noticed that α-particles (positively charged helium nuclei) easily penetrated mica without making holes in it as a bullet might. This led him to suspect that the α -particles were passing right through the atoms themselves rather than pushing atoms out of the way.

Rutherford also noticed that some of the α-particles were deflected out of their straight-line paths as they went through the mica, and he thought that this was caused by electric repulsion between the positively charged part of the mica atoms and the positive α-particles. Rutherford's students, Hans Geiger and Ernest Marsden, then carried out a series of experiments on the scattering of α-particles by thin metal films, as shown in the diagrams below.

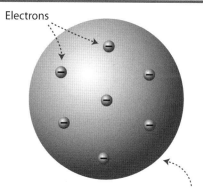

Uniform, positively charged sphere

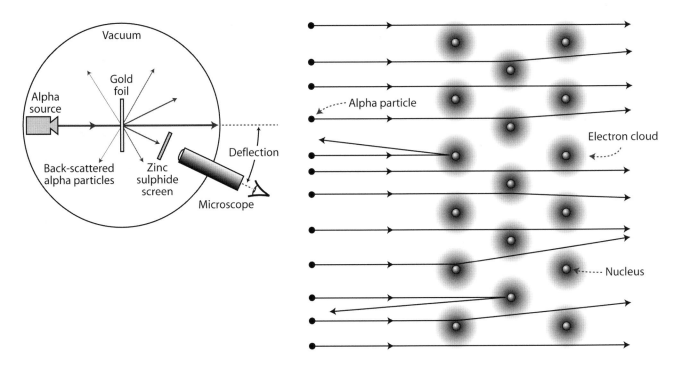

The most important of these experiments was with thin gold foil. A source of α-particles was contained in an evacuated chamber. The α-particles were incident on a thin gold foil (**a few hundred atoms thick**) whose plane was perpendicular to their direction of motion. The alpha particles were detected by the flashes of light (scintillations) they produced when they hit a fluorescent glass screen. The experiment **had to be carried out in a vacuum to prevent collisions between alpha particles and gas atoms** deflecting the alpha particles. The table outlines the results and Rutherford's conclusions.

Results Of Gold Foil Scattering Experiment	Rutherford's Conclusion
Most of the alpha particles were undeflected.	The majority of the alpha particles passed straight through the metal foil because they did not come close enough to any repulsive positive charge at all.
Some alpha particles were scattered by appreciable angles.	Only when a positive alpha particle approached sufficiently close to the nucleus, was it repelled strongly enough to rebound at high angles. Scattering was due to the mutual repulsion between the positive nucleus and the positive alpha particle. The small size of the nucleus explained the small number of alpha particles that were repelled in this way.
About 1 in 8000 alpha particles was 'back-scattered' through a very large angle indeed.	Back scattering occurs only when the incident alpha particle makes close to a "head-on" collision with a gold atom. Such collisions are quite rare because the nucleus of the atom is very small compared with the atom as a whole. Most of the atom is, in fact, empty space.

All the positive charge and most of the mass of an atom formed an exceptionally small, dense core or nucleus. The negative charge consisted of a "cloud of electrons" surrounding the positive nucleus.

The Size of a Nucleus

It was a challenging exercise for physicists to get some notion of the size of a nucleus by experiment. This is because the nucleus has a "fuzzy", rather than a sharp, edge. Nevertheless, physicists obtained an early idea of the size of a nucleus by firing α-particles at it. The distance of closest approach is an approximate upper limit of the size of a nucleus. Early experiments suggested that the nuclear radii were of the order of 10^{-15} m.

Variation of Nuclear Radius with Nucleon Number

Suppose we assume that the volume of a nucleon (proton or neutron) in any nucleus is about the same. Then the **volume of the nucleus is directly proportional to the total number of nucleons** contained within it (that is, the **mass number A**). If we also suppose the nucleus to be spherical, then

$$r = r_0 A^{1/3}$$

where   r = the radius of a given nucleus
   A = the mass number (number of nucleons within the nucleus)
   r_0 is the constant of proportionality

Observe that r_0 is **the constant of proportionality in the equation above**. However, it is also the radius of the nucleus for which A = 1, that is, it **is the radius of the proton**. The value of r_0 is found by experiment to be **about** 1.2×10^{-15} m or 1.2 fm or 1.2 fermi. However, r_0 is not a well-defined constant and different values are obtained using different experimental techniques.

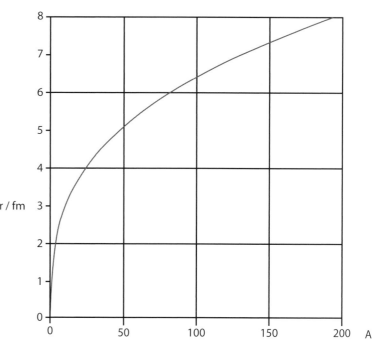

Nuclear Density

The density of nuclear matter is constant, that is, **all nuclei have the same density**. Suppose a nucleus of mass number, A, is spherical with radius r and that the mean mass of its nucleons is m. Then its total mass M is given by:

$$M = Am = \rho \frac{4\pi r^3}{3} = \rho \frac{4\pi r_0^3 A}{3} \text{ since } r = r_0 A^{1/3}$$

where ρ = the density of nuclear matter.

Dividing by A gives:

$$m = \frac{4\pi r_0^3 \rho}{3}$$

Hence the density of nuclear matter ρ is given by:

$$\rho = \frac{3m}{4\pi r_0^3}$$

which is a constant, independent of A.

If we substitute the known values for m (the mass of the proton, 1.66×10^{-27} kg) and the value for r_0 (1.2×10^{-15} m) we obtain the density of nuclear matter to be a staggering 2.3×10^{17} kg m^{-3}.

The huge density of nuclear matter in comparison with everyday matter is because there is a great deal of empty space in ordinary matter between the nucleus and the orbiting electrons, but there is no empty space between the particles inside the nucleus!

Readers should know that the **Notes for Guidance stipulate that candidates should be able to deduce the equation for ρ and appreciate the reason why its value is so large.**

Exercise 6

1. Your data and formulae sheet gives the equation for the radius of a nucleus as $r = r_0 A^{1/3}$
   (i) In this equation what does the symbol A represent?
   (ii) In terms of protons, neutrons and electrons, describe the structure of an atom of lithium–7 ($^{7}_{3}\text{Li}$).
   (iii) Use the equation to find the radius of a lithium–7 nucleus. Take $r_0 = 1.2$ fm.
   (iv) Hence find the density of a lithium–7 nucleus. (Mass of a lithium–7 nucleus = 7.014 u, sphere volume = $\frac{4\pi r^3}{3}$)
   (CCEA AY211 Summer 2011, modified)

2. (a) Experimental evidence for the existence of atomic nuclei was provided by the scattering of α particles through a thin gold foil. State two significant observations from the experiment and explain their significance.

(b) Equation 1 states the relationship between nuclear radius and atomic mass number.
r_0 is the mean nucleon radius and equals 1.2 fm.
$$r = r_0 A^{1/3} \qquad \textbf{Equation 1}$$
Equation 2 states the relationship between the volume of a sphere and its radius.
$$V = \frac{4\pi r^3}{3} \qquad \textbf{Equation 2}$$
   (i) Given that the mean mass of a nucleon is 1.66×10^{-27} kg, use **Equations 1** and **2** to determine the density of a $^{12}_{6}\text{C}$ (carbon 12) nucleus.
   (ii) Carbon 12 has an atomic density of 2.3 g cm^{-3}. Titanium 48 has an atomic density of 4.5 g cm^{-3}. State the nuclear density of titanium 48 and explain your reasoning.
   (CCEA AY211 January 2011, modified)

4.6 Nuclear Decay

Students should be able to:

4.6.1 Understand how the nature of alpha-particles, beta particles and gamma-radiation determines their penetration and range;

4.6.2 Calculate changes to nucleon number and proton number as a result of emissions;

4.6.3 Appreciate the random nature of radioactive decay;

4.6.4 Model with constant probability of decay, leading to exponential decay;

4.6.5 Use the equations $A = \lambda N$ and $A = A_0 e^{-\lambda t}$, where A is the activity;

4.6.6 Define half-life;

4.6.7 Use $T_{1/2} = \dfrac{0.693}{\lambda}$;

4.6.8 Describe an experiment to measure half-life;

The Nucleus

Here are some key facts about atomic nuclei:

- Every atom has a central positively charged nucleus with a diameters of around 10^{-15} m.
- Atomic diameters are around 10^{-10} m, so the atom is typically 100 000 times bigger than its nucleus.
- Over 99.9% of the mass of an atom is in its nucleus.
- Atomic nuclei are totally unaffected by chemical reactions.
- Nuclei contain protons and neutrons. These are collectively known as **nucleons**.

The properties of nucleons are compared with those of the electron in the table below.

	Electron	Proton	Neutron
Relative Mass*	$^{1}/_{1840}$	1	1
Actual Mass**	9.109×10^{-31} kg	1.673×10^{-31} kg or 1836 m_e	1.675×10^{-31} kg or 1839 m_e
Relative Charge	−1	+1	0
Charge	-1.60×10^{-19} C	$+1.60 \times 10^{-19}$ C	Zero

* relative to the proton   ** m_e is the mass of the electron.

Nucleons are held together by the **strong nuclear force** which only acts over very short distances. The strong nuclear force is much stronger than the electric force of repulsion that exists between protons within the nucleus. Here are some definitions:

Atomic Number, Z   this is the number of protons in the nucleus.
Mass Number, A   this is the total number of nucleons in the nucleus.

A nucleus is described using these two numbers and the **chemical symbol of the element**. The general form is: $_Z^A X$
So, the uranium nucleus (chemical symbol U) containing 92 protons and 143 neutrons has Z = 92 and A = 92 + 143 = 235.

The symbol is therefore $_{92}^{235}U$.

Isotopes

Isotopes are nuclei with the same number of protons but differing numbers of **neutrons.** This means the "bottom number" for isotopes of the same element must always be the same. So, for example, hydrogen has three stable isotopes, hydrogen (1p), deuterium (1p,1n) and tritium (1p, 2n). Their symbols are: $_1^1 H$, $_1^2 H$ and $_1^3 H$.

Radioactivity

Some elements have unstable isotopes whose nuclei disintegrate randomly and spontaneously. This effect known as **radioactivity**. Radioactive sources can emit any of three different types of radiation, α–particles, β–particles or γ–waves. The Becquerel (Bq) is the name given to the unit of activity. **1 Bq is 1 disintegration per second.**

Types of Radiation

Alpha (α) Particles	Beta (β) Particles	Gamma (γ) Waves
• An α-particle is a helium nucleus with two protons and two neutrons, and so has a mass number of 4. • The symbol for an α-particle is $_2^4 \alpha$ or $_2^4 He$ • α-particles are positively charged and so will be deflected in an electric or magnetic field. • α-particles have poor powers of penetration and can only travel through about 4 cm of air. • α-particles can easily be stopped by a sheet of paper. • Since α-particles move relatively slowly and have a high momentum they **interact with matter producing intense ionisation** – a typical α-particle can produce about **100 000 ion–pairs per cm of air** through which it passes. • α-decay is described by the equation below $_Z^A X \rightarrow {}_{Z-2}^{A-4} Y + {}_2^4 \alpha$	• A β-particle is a very fast electron and thus it has relative atomic mass of about $^1/_{1840}$. • The symbol for a β-particle is $_{-1}^{0}\beta$ or $_{-1}^{0}e$ • β-particles are emitted from nuclei where the number of neutrons is much larger than the number of protons – one of the neutrons changes into a proton and an electron. The proton remains inside the nucleus but the electron is immediately emitted from the nucleus as a β-particle. • The deflection of β-particles in an electric or magnetic field will be greater than that of α-particles, as the beta particles have much smaller mass to charge ratio. • β-particles interact less with matter than α-particles and have a greater penetrating power. • β-particles can travel several metres in air, but are stopped by 5 mm thick aluminium foil. • β-particles have an ionising power between that of alpha and gamma radiation. • The decay equation for β emission is shown below $_Z^A X \rightarrow {}_{Z+1}^{A} Y + {}_{-1}^{0}\beta$	• Unlike the other types of radiation, γ-radiation does not consist of particles. • γ-rays are short wavelength, high energy electromagnetic radiation emitted from unstable nuclei. • The wavelength of γ-rays is characteristic of the nuclide that emits it. The wavelengths of γ-rays are typically in the region 10^{-10} to 10^{-12} m. • Like α and β radiation, γ radiation comes from a disintegrating unstable nucleus. • γ-radiation has no mass. • Electric and magnetic fields have no effect on γ-radiation. • γ-radiation has great penetrating power, travelling several metres in air. • A thick block of lead or concrete is used to greatly reduce the effects of gamma radiation, but cannot stop it completely. A lead block about 5 cm thick will absorb around 90% of the γ-rays. • Gamma radiation has the weakest ionising power as it interacts least with matter. • The decay equation for γ-emission is shown below $_Z^A X^* \rightarrow {}_Z^A X + \gamma$ *The asterisk indicates that the parent nuclide is in an excited state.

Worked Example

(a) *Complete the table below by inserting appropriate values of mass and charge for the alpha particle, the beta particle and the gamma radiation.*

	Mass / u	Charge / C
Alpha particle		
Beta particle		
Gamma radiation		

(b) (i) *How do these decay particles lose their kinetic energy after release into the atmosphere?*

(ii) *Explain why the alpha particle has a shorter range in air than the beta particle even though it is released with more kinetic energy.*

(c) *The diagram below represents the decay chain of protactinium 236 to radium 228 in three consecutive stages r, s and t.*

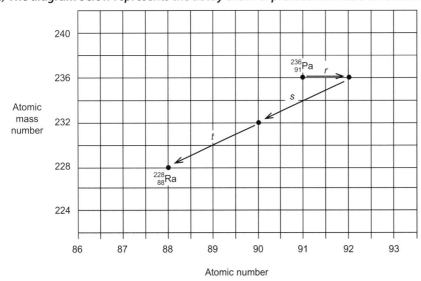

Identify the decay processes r, s and t. Explain your reasoning.

CCEA AY211 Summer 2010 (modified)

(a)

	Mass / u	Charge / C
Alpha particle	4	3.2×10^{-19}
Beta particle	$1/1840$	-1.6×10^{-19}
Gamma radiation	0	0

(b) (i) Collisions between the particles and the molecules of the medium cause energy to be transferred from the decay particle to the molecules.

(ii) Larger mass of the alpha particle means that it loses more momentum per collision.

(c) r is β decay since atomic number increases by 1. s and t are both α decay since in both cases the atomic number decreases by 2 and the mass number decreases by 4.

Law of Radioactive Decay

The rate of decay of a particular species (nuclide) is directly proportional to the number of unstable nuclei of that nuclide present. Therefore if there are **N** unstable nuclei present at time **t**:

Rate of Disintegration with time = Activity, $\mathbf{A = -\lambda N}$

where λ = a constant of proportionality called the decay constant. It is measured in units of s^{-1}.

The minus sign is present because as t increases N decreases. The rate of disintegration of unstable nuclei is called **the activity** of the source. Activity is measured in disintegrations per second or Becquerel (Bq).

Two mathematical consequences of this law are:

$$\mathbf{A = A_o e^{-\lambda t}} \quad \text{and} \quad \mathbf{N = N_o e^{-\lambda t}}$$

where A_o = the initial activity at time t = 0

A = the activity at a time t = t

N_o = the original number of radioactive nuclei

N = the number of radioactive nuclei at time t = t

The **activity, A, and the number of radioactive nuclei, N, decrease exponentially** with time.

Half–Life (T$_{\frac{1}{2}}$)

The half–life of a radioactive material is the time taken for the activity of that material to fall to half of its original value. A mathematical consequence of this definition is that:

$$T_{\frac{1}{2}} = \frac{\ln 2}{\lambda} \approx \frac{0.693}{\lambda}$$

An equally acceptable definition for the half–life of a radioactive nuclide is **the time taken for half those radioactive nuclei present to disintegrate**.

<hr>

Worked Example

The half–life of cobalt–60, a typical laboratory γ–source, is 5.26 years. What mass of cobalt–60 will have an activity of 8.72×10⁵ Bq? Take the mass of a cobalt–60 atom to be 9.96×10⁻²⁶ kg.

CCEA AY211 Summer 2011 (modified)

$$T_{\frac{1}{2}} = \frac{\ln 2}{\lambda} \textbf{ so } \lambda = \frac{\ln 2}{T_{\frac{1}{2}}} = \frac{0.693}{5.26 \times 365 \times 24 \times 3600} = 4.178 \times 10^{-9} \text{ s}^{-1}$$

$$N = \frac{A}{\lambda} = \frac{8.72 \times 10^5}{4.178 \times 10^{-9}} = 2.087 \times 10^{14} \text{ atoms}$$

So mass $= 2.087 \times 10^{14} \times 9.96 \times 10^{-26} = 2.079 \times 10^{-11}$ kg

<hr>

Measuring the Half–life of a Radioactive Substance

The easiest method involves the use of a Geiger–Muller (GM) tube, a scaler or ratemeter and a source of protactinium (234–Pa). This isotope of protactinium emits β–particles. When alpha, beta or gamma radiation enters the GM tube, it causes some of the argon gas inside to ionise and give an electrical discharge. This discharge is detected and counted by the counter. If the counter is connected to its internal speaker, you can hear the click when radiation enters the tube.

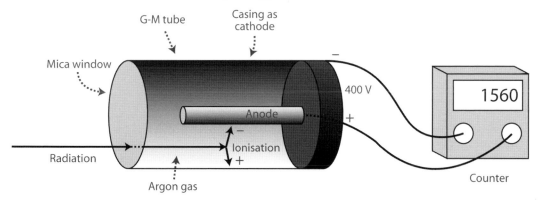

However, even in the absence of all known sources of radioactivity, the GM tube and counter still detects radiation. This is known as **background radiation** and it comes from the Sun, cosmic rays from space, hospital nuclear physics departments, nuclear power stations, granite rocks and so on. Before we use a GM tube to carry out any quantitative work on radiation we must first measure the background radiation if we are to correct for it in our experiment.

To Measure the Background Radiation
- First remove known sources of radiation from the laboratory, then set the GM counter to zero.
- Switch on the counter and start a stopwatch. After 30 minutes read the count on the counter.
- Divide the count by 30 to obtain the background count rate in counts per minute. A typical figure is around 15 counts per minute. This background count must always be subtracted from any other count when measuring the activity from a specific source.

Setting up the Protactinium Source
Protactinium–234 is one of the decay products of uranium-238 and any compound of uranium-238 will have within it traces of protactinium. These traces may be conveniently extracted from it by chemical means. The protactinium decays by β–emission into another long–lived isotope of uranium (234-U) which is itself α–emitting. The very long half–life indicates low activity, which is not enough to interfere with this experiment. Moreover, the α–particles which are emitted will not penetrate a polythene bottle containing the protactinium. The β–activity at any instant of the extracted solution can therefore be used as a measure of the quantity of protactinium still present in it.

A thin–walled polythene bottle is filled with equal volumes of an acid solution of uranyl nitrate and pentyl ethanoate. When the liquids are shaken up together the organic ethanoate removes most of the protactinium present.

The solutions are not miscible and the protactinium remains in the upper layer when the liquids have once more separated.

The β–activity of the protactinium is observed with a GM tube and ratemeter, and the count–rate is recorded at 10 second intervals.

Allowance is then made for the background count of the GM tube. If, for example, the measured rate with the GM tube and ratemeter is 32 counts/minute and the background rate is 15 counts/minute, then the corrected count rate is 32 – 15 = 17 counts/minute.

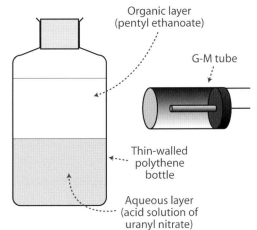

Organic layer (pentyl ethanoate)

G-M tube

Thin-walled polythene bottle

Aqueous layer (acid solution of uranyl nitrate)

Treatment of the Results to Find the Half–life of Protactinium

The corrected count rate of the protactinium is taken as a measure of its activity, A. By the Law of Radioactive Decay:

$$A = A_0 e^{-\lambda t}$$

Taking natural logs of both sides gives:

$$\ln A = \ln A_0 - \lambda t$$

Comparing this last equation with that for a straight line:

$$y = c + mx$$

we see that a graph of ln A (y-axis) against time (x-axis) is a straight line of gradient $-\lambda$ and y-axis intercept at ln A_0

We therefore plot a graph of **ln A** (y-axis) against **time** (x-axis), draw the straight line of best fit and determine its gradient ($-\lambda$). We then find the half–life by calculating the value of $\dfrac{0.693}{\lambda}$.

The generally accepted value for the half–life of protactinium–234 is 68 seconds.

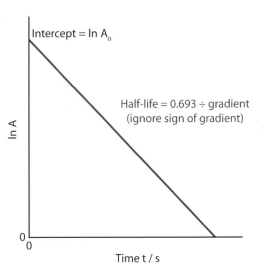

Intercept = ln A_0

Half-life = 0.693 ÷ gradient (ignore sign of gradient)

ln A

0

Time t / s

4.7 Nuclear Energy

Students should be able to:

4.7.1 Appreciate the equivalence of mass and energy;

4.7.2 Recall the equation **E = mc²** and understand that it applies to all energy changes;

4.7.3 Use **E = Δmc²** in nuclear calculations;

4.7.4 Know how the binding energy per nucleon varies with mass number;

4.7.5 Describe the principles of fission and fusion with reference to the binding energy per nucleon curve

Equivalence Of Mass And Energy

In 1905 Albert Einstein published "The Special Theory of Relativity", which dealt with the speed of light for observers moving with a constant velocity relative to each other. For us, the important assertion made by Einstein was that **there is an equivalence to a mass, m and energy, E** given by the equation **E = mc²**, where c is the speed of light in a vacuum.

The Electron–Volt (eV) and the Unified Atomic Mass Unit (u)

The joule and the kilogram are much too large to be useful when dealing with atomic and nuclear processes. A much more appropriate unit for energy is the **electron–volt** (eV). The electron volt is the kinetic energy possessed by an electron accelerated from rest through a voltage of one volt.

For our purposes it is sufficient to know that:

1 eV = 1.6×10⁻¹⁹ J

1 MeV = 1 million electron – volts = 1.6×10⁻¹³ J

The unit commonly used for mass when dealing with atomic and nuclear processes is the unified atomic mass unit (abbreviated to "u").

1 u = $\dfrac{1}{12}$ of the mass of the carbon-12 atom = 1.66 × 10⁻²⁷ kg

Mass Defect

The mass of a nucleus is **always less** than the sum of the masses of its constituent nucleons. This difference in mass is called the **mass defect** of the nucleus.

Mass defect = Total mass of the nucleons – Mass of the nucleus

This reduction in mass arises due to the combining of the nucleons to form the nucleus. When the nucleons are combined to form a nucleus a tiny portion of their mass is converted to energy. This energy is called the **binding energy (BE)** of the nucleus. Binding energies are usually quoted in MeV.

The binding energy of a nucleus is the amount of energy that has to be *supplied* to separate the nucleons completely i.e. to an infinite distance apart.

The **binding energy per nucleon** is a useful measure of the stability of a nucleus. The average binding energy per nucleon varies with nucleon number as shown below. A graph of average binding energy per nucleon against atomic number has a similar shape.

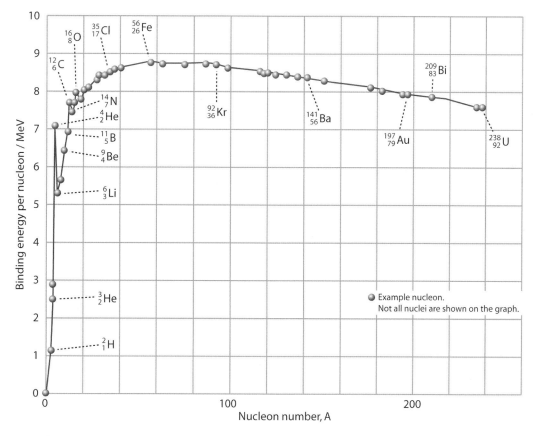

Worked Example

Calculate (i) the binding energy and (ii) binding energy per nucleon of Helium-4. The masses of the neutron and proton are 1.0087 u and 1.0078 u respectively. The mass of the helium nucleus is 4.0026 u.

(i) The He–4 nucleus contains 2 protons and 2 neutrons.

mass of 2 protons	$= 2 \times 1.0078$ u $= 2.0156$ u
mass of 2 neutrons	$= 2 \times 1.0087$ u $= 2.0174$ u
mass of the constituent nucleons	$= 4.0330$ u
mass of the helium nucleus	$= 4.0026$ u

Therefore, mass defect $= 4.0330 - 4.0026 = 0.0304$ u $= 0.0304 \times 1.66 \times 10^{-27}$ kg

Binding energy $= mc^2 = 0.0304 \times 1.66 \times 10^{-27} \times (3 \times 10^8)^2 = 4.54 \times 10^{-12}$ J

We have to convert the unit from joules to MeV, so:

Binding energy $= 4.54 \times 10^{-12} \div 1.6 \times 10^{-13} =$ **28.39 MeV**

(ii) **Binding energy per nucleon** = binding energy ÷ no. of nucleons = $28.38 \div 4 =$ **7.1 MeV per nucleon**

Fusion is the joining of lighter nuclei to produce a heavier and more stable nucleus. Nuclei to the left of the peak of the BE/nucleon against nucleon number curve (above) undergo fusion to increase stability by reaching a higher BE per nucleon.

The fusion process results in the release of energy since the average binding energy of these fusion products is higher than that of the lighter nuclei which join together.

In fusion some of the mass of the lighter nuclei is converted to kinetic energy of the fusion product. This means that the mass of the heavier nucleus is less than the total masses of the two light nuclei that fuse.

The reaction cannot take place at room temperature because of the repulsive electric force between the positively charged nuclei.

It only occurs when the speed of the colliding nuclei is great enough for the nuclei to overcome this repulsive force and they can come close enough for the attractive, but very short range, strong nuclear force to cause fusion to occur.

For example, hydrogen nuclei can fuse, as shown on the right, only when the temperature is high enough (about 15 million degrees Celsius).

At such high temperatures matter exists in a fourth state known as **plasma**. The atomic electrons break free from the nucleus, and the gas–like fluid is a mixture of electrons, positive ions and free nuclei.

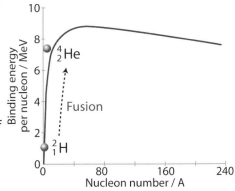

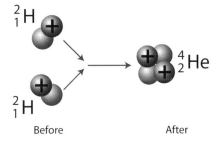

Before   After

Fission is the deep division of a massive nucleus into two less massive nuclei, each with a higher binding energy per nucleon.

Nuclei to the right of the peak of the BE/nucleon against nucleon number curve (above) undergo fission to increase stability by reaching a higher BE per nucleon.

The total binding energy of these fission fragments is higher than that of the heavy nucleus.

Due to the increase in the total binding energy, some of the mass of the heavy nucleus is converted to kinetic energy of the fission fragments.

For example, uranium-235 undergoes fission when it absorbs a neutron, as shown on the right.

Neutrons produced in the fission process can go on to cause further fissions in a **chain reaction**.

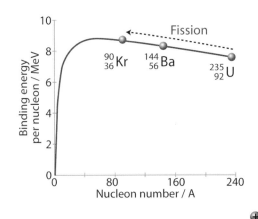

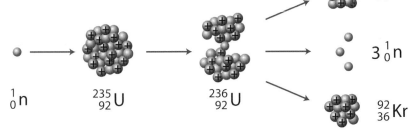

Exercise 8

1. A camera battery is charged at 4.2 V, 0.7A for 90 minutes. This results in a transfer of energy. Use the Einstein mass–energy relationship to find the small mass increase of the battery.

(CCEA AY211 Summer 2011, modified)

2. One example of the fission of U–235 is the following reaction:

$$^{235}_{92}U + ^{1}_{0}n \rightarrow ^{140}_{55}Cs + ^{93}_{37}Rb + 3^{1}_{0}n + energy$$

(i) Calculate the amount of energy released, in joules, in this reaction.

Mass of U-235 atom = 235.04394 u
Mass of Rb-93 atom = 92.92204 u
Mass of Cs-140 atom = 139.91728 u
Mass of a neutron = 1.008665 u

(ii) Estimate the theoretical maximum energy released if 1 kg of uranium-235 underwent fission by this route.

(CCEA AY211 Summer 2011, modified)

4.8 Nuclear Fission

Students should be able to:

4.8.1 Describe a fission reactor in terms of chain reaction, critical size, moderators, control rods, cooling system and reactor shielding.

The Nuclear Fission Reactor

An **uncontrolled** fission chain reaction in uranium is brought about in an atomic bomb. A **fission reactor** is an arrangement in which nuclear fission is **controlled** in such a way that heat can be safely extracted to produce steam to drive a turbine and produce electricity. How do physicists bring about the conditions in which controlled nuclear fission can occur?

The common features of the fission processes in common nuclear reactors are:

- It always releases huge quantities of energy, about 80% of which is carried away by the kinetic energy of the two major fission fragments.
- The fission fragments are often radioactive and their subsequent decay accounts for about 10% of the total energy released.
- Extremely penetrating and highly dangerous gamma rays are always produced along with the fission fragments. These gamma rays and the kinetic energy of the sub-atomic particles produced account for the remaining energy released.
- Further neutrons are always produced, on average around 2.5 per fission. These additional neutrons can go on to produce further fission events, yielding more neutrons which produce even more fission events and so on. In this way fission has the potential to produce a chain reaction.

There are **four common types** of nuclear reactor:

1. Britain's oldest nuclear reactors were of the **Magnox type**, so-called because the natural **uranium** fuel was clad in a tube made of magnesium alloy.
2. **Advanced Gas-cooled Reactors** (AGRs) use circulating gas (almost invariably carbon dioxide) as the coolant.
3. **Pressurised Water Reactors** (PWRs) use water under such high pressure that even at a temperature of over 200°C it is still not boiling.
4. **Fast Reactors** use plutonium rather than uranium as the fuel and the coolant is circulating liquid sodium. Fast reactors tend to be used in nuclear–powered submarines.

Because the AGR is now the most common type of reactor used in the UK, our future discussion will be limited to that reactor type.

Fuel Enrichment and Neutron Moderation

Natural uranium consists of about 99.3% uranium-238 and 0.7% uranium-235. Uranium-238 is fissile, but only with very fast neutrons. Uranium-235 is fissile only with slow neutrons (called thermal neutrons).

Fission neutrons are too fast to cause fission in uranium-235, so they **need to be slowed down. The neutrons are slowed down by the use of a material called a moderator**, of which the most common are graphite, water (H_2O) and heavy water (deuterium oxide or D_2O).

To make the uranium within the reactor more likely to undergo fission with slow neutrons it needs to be **enriched** by raising the proportion of fissile uranium-235 from about 0.7% in the natural ore to about 3% in the nuclear fuel rods.

The AGR is an example of a **graphite moderated reactor**. The enriched uranium is in long, sealed tubes, called **fuel rods** which are arranged inside a block of graphite. The neutrons released by the fission of uranium-235 collide inelastically with the atoms of the graphite moderator and are slowed down to a speed where they are more likely to cause further fission in uranium-235 than be absorbed by the uranium-238. Below is a schematic diagram of an AGR nuclear fission reactor.

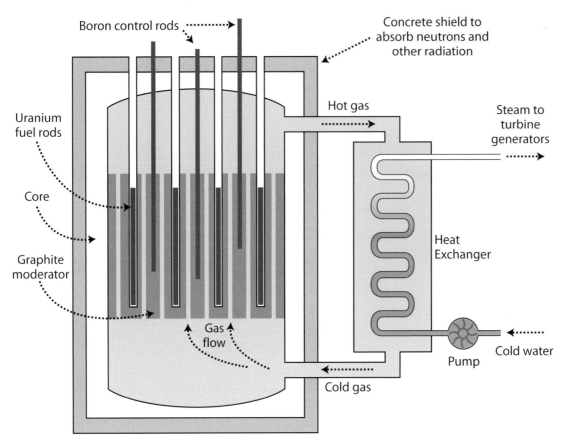

Critical Size

When a fission event occurs, there are three possible fates for the fission neutrons produced:
• they might escape from the fuel rod without causing a further fission;
• they might be absorbed by a neighbouring nucleus, again without causing fission;
• they cause another fission event in a uranium nucleus.

For the reaction to be sustained, on average at least one of the neutrons released by each fission event must go on to produce a further fission. The bigger the size of the uranium fuel assembly, the more likely it is that a fission neutron will go on to produce another fission event.

We can define the **critical size** of the fuel assembly as that which is just capable of sustaining a chain reaction within it. Below the critical size, too many of the neutrons which might have induced further fission escape and the chain reaction dies away. A typical nuclear power station has a fuel assembly which is around 5% above the critical size.

Control Rods

If, on average, much more than one of the neutrons produced by fission went on to cause further fission, then the reaction would quickly go out of control. So, **boron–coated steel rods, called control rods, are used to absorb excessive neutrons** before they can cause fission. When the control rods are lowered into the reactor the number of available neutrons is decreased and fewer fission events can occur.

Electricity Production

The heat energy produced by the fission reaction is removed by passing a coolant through the reactor. This coolant then passes its energy to the water flowing through a **heat exchanger**, producing steam to drive **the turbines** which turn the **electricity–producing generators**. The part of a nuclear power station associated with the turbines and generators is exactly the same as would be seen in a conventional power station burning fossil fuels.

Reactor Shielding

Around every civil reactor is a very thick concrete shield to prevent potentially dangerous radiation, particularly very penetrating gamma waves and neutrons, from reaching the operating personnel and the wider community.

Exercise 9

The diagram shows a simplified diagram for a fission reactor.

(i) Explain briefly the purpose and name a suitable material
   for: 1. the moderator
       2. the control rods

(ii) Why must the total amount of uranium in the reactor
    core be greater than the critical size?

(iii) Why must the total amount of uranium in a fuel rod be
    less than the critical size?

(CCEA AY211 January 2011, modified)

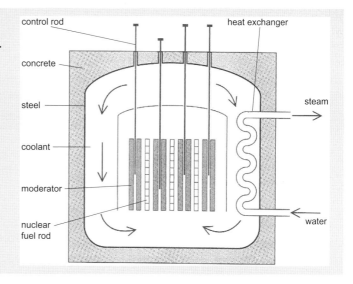

4.9 Nuclear Fusion

Students should be able to:

4.9.1 Understand the conditions required for nuclear fusion;

4.9.2 Estimate the temperature required for fusion;

4.9.3 Describe the following methods of plasma confinement: gravitational, inertial and magnetic;

4.9.4 Appreciate the difficulties of achieving fusion on a practical terrestrial scale;

4.9.5 Describe the JET fusion reactor; and

4.9.6 State the D-T reaction and appreciate why this is most suitable for terrestrial fusion.

Fusion in the Stars

Almost all of the energy we receive on Earth comes from the Sun as a result of thermonuclear fusion. All the elements which form the basis of our material world as well as the material in all living things on the Earth were formed by fusion in stars.

The Sun consists mainly of hydrogen and helium. At the core of the Sun the temperature is many millions of kelvins resulting in a constant fusion of hydrogen nuclei. The reactions can be summarised by:

$$_1^1H + _1^1H + _1^1H + _1^1H \rightarrow _1^4He + \text{other products} + \text{energy}$$

To overcome the electrostatic repulsion between nuclei, they need to have sufficient kinetic energy. This requires temperatures of the order of 10^8 or 10^9 K. At such temperatures matter exists in a fourth state known as **plasma**. The atomic electrons break free from the nucleus, and the gas–like fluid is a mixture of electrons, positive ions and free nuclei.

Estimate of the Temperature Required for Fusion

If the protons are projected towards each other the repulsion between their positive charges causes their kinetic energy to decrease and their potential energy to increase. The energy needed to bring a pair of protons sufficiently close to bring about fusion is about **110 keV.** We can use this information to calculate the temperature to which the proton assembly must be heated.

We recall from section 4.2.7 of the specification that the temperature of a gas is a measure of the mean kinetic energy of the gas molecules and that:

$$\text{Mean Kinetic Energy} = \frac{1}{2}m\langle c^2\rangle = \frac{3kT}{2}$$

where   m = the mass of each particle

$\langle c^2 \rangle$ = the mean square speed

k = Boltzmann's constant
T = temperature in K

If we treat the collection of protons as a gas, of mean kinetic energy 110 keV (where 1 keV = 1.6×10^{-16} J), then:

$$T = \frac{2 \times \text{mean kinetic energy}}{3 \times k} = \frac{2 \times 110 \times 1.6\times10^{-16}}{3 \times 1.38\times10^{-23}} = 850\times10^6 \text{ K}$$

Plasma Confinement

Fusion on a practical terrestrial scale requires a temperature of 850 million kelvins. There is no possibility of using a conventional reaction vessel as its walls would simply vaporise.

There are three possible methods to confine the plasma long enough for fusion to occur:

Gravitational Confinement	Inertial Confinement	Magnetic Confinement
• **Gravitational forces in stars can provide the plasma confinement.** • the inward gravitational pull balances the outward forces created by pressure of the plasma and radiation pressure (photons impacting on the particles of the gas plasma and exerting an outward pressure). • **gravitational confinement would not work on the Earth** since we require an enormous mass of material to provide gravitational forces strong enough to balance the forces tending to dissipate the plasma.	• **inertial confinement** involves **using intense ion or laser beams** directed at **a solid fuel pellet** (such as lithium hydride). • **the laser beams provide the energy to heat the material to the temperature required for fusion.** • the idea is to produce fusion for long enough to extract the energy before the plasma escapes: rather like pulling a table-cloth away from a table before the tea-cups fall over! • The fusion seen in this situation is of the type: $$^{6}_{3}\text{Li} + ^{2}_{1}\text{H} \rightarrow 2\,^{4}_{2}\text{He}$$	• **Magnetic confinement** uses magnetic fields to hold the plasma. • The magnetic field is produced by electric current flowing in a coil wound into a shape known as **toroid** (doughnut). • The magnetic field produced is circular within the highly evacuated toroidal chamber. • The charged particles in the plasma are moving in a magnetic field and experience a force. • The force causes charged plasma particles to circulate endlessly in helical paths around the magnetic field lines produced by water–cooled toroidal field coils.

How is a Magnetically Confined Plasma Heated?

A plasma is a good conductor of electricity. The plasma acts like the secondary coil of a large transformer. The current in the primary coil induces a current in the circulating plasma which heats the particles (transformer heating action).

Current in toroidal field coils produces the magnetic field needed to confine the plasma within the "doughnut". This is the principle of the JET (Joint European Torus) based in Oxford, England.

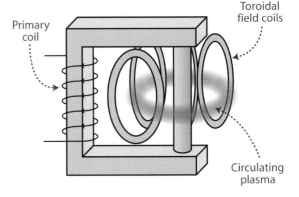

Primary coil

Toroidal field coils

Circulating plasma

Why Have We Not Yet Achieved Controlled Thermonuclear Fusion?

It is necessary to hold the plasma well away from the container walls to avoid vapourising them. This is technically very challenging. The plasma must be kept at a sufficiently high temperature for long enough to obtain adequate numbers of fusion reactions. To date temperatures of 10^7 K have only been achieved for fractions of a second. Researchers must also ensure that the energy produced by fusion exceeds that supplied by the operators to maintain the reactor at its enormously high temperature.

The Deuterium–Tritium (or D–T) Reaction

The process with greatest promise at the moment is known as the **deuterium–tritium (or D–T) reaction:**

$$^{2}_{1}\text{H} + ^{3}_{1}\text{H} \rightarrow 2\,^{4}_{2}\text{He} + ^{1}_{0}\text{n} + 17.6 \text{ MeV}$$

Surrounding the reactor is a blanket of lithium. Lithium can absorb the fusion neutron and then fission according to the reaction:

$$^{7}_{3}\text{Li} + ^{1}_{0}\text{n} \rightarrow ^{4}_{2}\text{He} + ^{3}_{1}\text{H} + ^{1}_{0}\text{n}$$

The neutrons released in both reactions above can go on to sustain a chain reaction in lithium, thus converting the lithium into tritium fuel for the D–T process. The heat from the kinetic energy given to the helium nuclei would then heat water to give steam, which then would be used to drive turbine-generators.

The D–T process is attractive because:

- The D–T reaction is a single–stage reaction which produces a much greater energy release than others of similar type, e.g. D–D fusion and at a lower fusion temperature.
- There is a ready supply of fuel (deuterium from seawater and tritium from lithium).
- There are only limited hazardous waste products (neutron irradiated materials), so there is no need for long-term storage of hazardous radioactive waste (as with current fission reactors).
- There is a considerable energy yield per fusion (and hence per kg of fuel used).

Exercise 10

Nuclear fusion could replace fossil fuels as an energy resource on the Earth.

(a) One reaction which could lead to the release of energy is the fusion of deuterium and tritium (the D–T reaction).
   (i) Give the equation for the D–T reaction.
   (ii) Give two reasons why this reaction is most suitable for terrestrial fusion.

(b) (i) The JET fusion reactor has been designed to produce the required conditions for fusion to take place. Outline the basic principles of its operation.
   (ii) Explain why it is difficult to achieve fusion in the JET fusion reactor.

(CCEA AY211 June 2011, modified)

Unit 5 (A2 2)
Fields and their applications

5.1 Fields of Force

Students should be able to:

5.1.1 Explain the concept of a field of force

- A **field of force** is a region of space within which objects with a particular property experience a force.
- A **gravitational field** is a region of space within which a mass will experience a force.
- An **electrical field** is a region of space within which a charge will experience a force.
- A **magnetic field** is a region of space within which a moving charge will experience a force.
- Around every charge there exists an electric field, around every mass there exists a gravitational field and around moving charges there exists a magnetic field.

5.2 Gravitational Fields

Students should be able to:

5.2.1 Define gravitational field strength;

5.2.2 Recall and use the equation $g = F/m$;

5.2.3 State Newton's law of universal gravitation;

5.2.4 Recall and use the equation for the gravitational force between two pint masses, $F = \dfrac{Gm_1m_2}{r^2}$;

5.2.5 Recall and apply the equation for gravitational field strength $g = \dfrac{Gm}{r^2}$ and use this equation to calculate the mass of the Earth;

5.2.6 Apply knowledge of circular motion to planetary and satellite motion;

5.2.7 Show that the mathematical form of Kepler's third law is consistent with the law of universal gravitation;

5.2.8 State the period of a geostationary satellite.

Newton's Law of Universal Gravitation

Newton's Law of Universal Gravitation states that **between every two point masses there exists an attractive gravitational force which is directly proportional to the mass of each and inversely proportional to the square of their separation**. This is written mathematically as:

$$F = \frac{Gm_1m_2}{r^2}$$ where: m_1 and m_2 = the respective point masses, in kg

r = the distance between them, in m

G = a constant known as the universal gravitational constant which is equal to 6.67×10^{-11} N m^2 kg^{-2}

Gravitational Field Lines

The direction of a gravitational field line at a point shows the direction of the gravitational force on a mass of 1 kg at that point. For a uniform sphere the gravitational field pattern is described as **radially inwards**, because all field lines appear to converge at the centre of mass of the sphere.

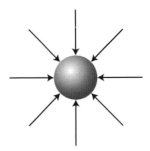

For a person on the Earth the field lines strike the surface at right angles. The radius of the Earth is so large that the field lines appear parallel and equally spaced. Such a field is called a **uniform field**.

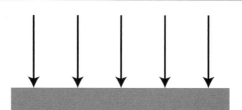

Gravitational Field Strength

Gravitational field strength at a point is equal to the force which would be produced on a test mass of 1 kg at that point. The diagram shows a point mass M. The gravitational force on a mass of 1 kg at the point X is given by:

$$F = \frac{G \times M \times 1}{r^2} = \frac{GM}{r^2}$$

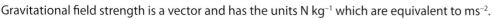

Since $g = \dfrac{F}{m}$, and m =1 in this example, we can have: $g = \dfrac{GM}{r^2}$

Gravitational field strength is a vector and has the units N kg^{-1} which are equivalent to ms^{-2}.

The weight of this 1 kg object is due to the gravitational attraction of the Earth:

$$W = mg = \frac{G \times M_E \times 1}{R_E^{\,2}}$$ where M_E = the mass of the Earth, in kg
R_E = the radius of the Earth, in m

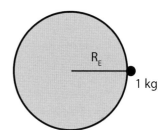

The Mass of the Earth

The average value of g over the surface of the Earth is generally taken as 9.81 ms^{-2}. The radius of the Earth is around 6400 km. Substitution of values for G and R_E into the above equation gives a mass M_E of 6×10^{24} kg.

Kepler's Third Law of Planetary Motion and Newton's Law of Gravitation

Using observations of the planets recorded by Tycho Brahe (1546-1601), Johannes Kepler published a number of laws between 1609 and 1619. Kepler's Third Law states that the square of the period of revolution of the planets about the Sun is directly proportional to the cube of their mean distances from it.

Consider a planet of mass m moving about the Sun in a circular orbit of radius, r. Suppose the angular velocity of the planet is ω and the mass of the Sun is M_S and the mass of the planet is m.

The centripetal force needed to keep the planet in orbit is provided by the gravitational attraction between the sun and the planet.

The orbital period of the planet, $T = \dfrac{2\pi}{\omega}$ giving $\omega = \dfrac{2\pi}{T}$

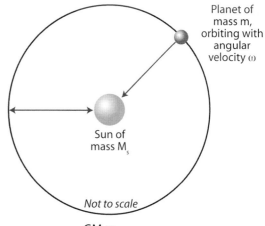

Planet of mass m, orbiting with angular velocity ω

Sun of mass M_S

Not to scale

Since gravity provides the centripetal force between the planet and the Sun: $F = mr\omega^2 = \dfrac{GM_S m}{r^2}$

Substituting $\omega = \dfrac{2\pi}{T}$ gives: $\dfrac{4\pi^2 rm}{T^2} = \dfrac{GM_S m}{r^2}$

Rearranging this gives: $T^2 = \dfrac{4\pi^2 r^3}{GM_S}$

Since G, M_S and π are constant regardless of the planet being considered, $\dfrac{T^2}{r^3}$ = a constant.

Note carefully:
• This relationship between T^2 and r^3 appears in any situation in which one body orbits another.
• In the case of the Earth in orbit around the Sun the mass is M_S, the mass of the sun.
• For the Moon in orbit around the Earth the mass is therefore M_E, the mass of the Earth.

Satellite Motion

For a satellite of mass m, in a circular orbit around the Earth in the equatorial plane and at a distance r from the Earth's centre the gravitational attraction between the satellite and the Earth provides the centripetal force. The relationship between orbital period and orbital radius derived above can be used. Since the satellite is in orbit around the Earth the mass of the Earth M_E is used.

Worked Example

Calculate the orbital period of a satellite in a close orbit of 200 km above the Earth's surface.
Use the following data: $M_E = 6.0\times10^{24}$ kg, $R_E = 6400$ km

The radius of the orbit r = 200 km plus the radius of the Earth, $R_E = 6400$ km

$r = 2\times10^5 + 6.4\times10^6$ m $= 6.6\times10^6$ m

$G = 6.67\times10^{-11}$ N m² kg⁻²

Using $T^2 = \dfrac{4\pi^2 r^3}{GM_E} = \dfrac{4\pi^2(6.67\times10^{-11})^3}{6.67\times10^{-11} \times 6.0\times10^{24}} = 28367893$

So T = 5326 s (approximately 89 minutes)

Worked Example

A geostationary satellite has an orbital period of 24 hours. Find the radius of a geogstationary orbit around the Earth.
Use the following data: $M_E = 6.0\times10^{24}$ kg, $R_E = 6400$ km

$G = 6.67\times10^{-11}$ N m² kg⁻²

Using $T^2 = \dfrac{4\pi^2 r^3}{GM_E}$ gives: $86400^2 = \dfrac{4\pi^2 \times r^3}{6.67\times10^{-11} \times 6.0\times10^{24}}$

Giving $r^3 = 7.575\times10^{22}$

So r = 42311739 m (approximately 42 300 km)

Exercise 11

1. (a) State Newton's law of universal gravitation.
   (b) The International Space Station of mass m_s, orbits the Earth at a height h above the Earth's surface. Take the Earth's mass as m_E and radius r_E.
   (i) State an equation for the gravitational force F which exists between the International Space Station and the Earth.

   (ii) Calculate the value of the Earth's gravitational field strength g at a height 350 km above the Earth's surface. Take the mass of the Earth to be 6.0×10^{24} kg and the mean radius of the Earth to be 6400 km.

   (iii) Explain why an astronaut in the International Space Station experiences apparent weightlessness, even though the Earth's gravitational field acts on him.

(CCEA AY221 Summer 2010)

2. (a) What is a gravitational field?
   (b) Calculate the mass of the Earth if the gravitational field strength at the Earth's surface is 9.81 N kg⁻¹ and the mean radius of the Earth is 6.37×10^3 km.

   (c) (i) "GOES–10" is the name given to one of the Geostationary Operational Environmental Satellites that the USA uses to monitor weather. Its orbital radius is 3.58×10^4 km **above the Earth's surface**. State the period of a geostationary satellite, give your answer in seconds.

   (ii) "GOES–10" has a mass of 2.11×10^3 kg. Calculate the centripetal force required to keep it moving in this orbit. Remember the mean radius of the Earth is 6.37×10^3 km.

   (iii) When this satellite reaches the end of its useful life it is boosted out of its geosynchronous orbit into a higher orbit. Determine the satellite's new period if the new orbit has a radius of 6.22×10^4 km above the Earth.

(CCEA AY221 Summer 2011)

3. (a) State, in words, Newton's law of gravitation.
   (b) Using Newton's law of gravitation, show that the period T of revolution of a satellite is related to the radius r of the orbit by the equation below:

$$T^2 = \dfrac{4\pi^2 r^3}{GM_S}$$

where M is the mass of the planet that is being orbited.

   (c) In this part of the question, use the following data:
   Radius of Earth = 6.37×10^6 m
   Mass of Earth = 5.98×10^{24} kg

   (i) A satellite orbits the Earth in a geostationary orbit. What is meant by a geostationary orbit?
   (ii) Calculate the height of the satellite above the Earth's surface.
   (iii) Calculate the linear velocity of the geostationary satellite.

(CCEA AY221 January 2010)

5.3 Electric Fields

Students should be able to:

5.3.1 Define electric field strength;

5.3.2 Recall and use the equation $E = \dfrac{F}{q}$;

5.3.3 State Coulomb's law for the force between point charges;

5.3.4 Recall and use the equation for the force between two point charges $F = \dfrac{q_1 q_2}{4\pi\varepsilon_0 r^2} = k\dfrac{q_1 q_2}{r^2}$ where $k = \dfrac{1}{4\pi\varepsilon_0}$

5.3.5 State that ε_0 is the permittivity of a vacuum and determine its SI base units;

5.3.6 Recall and use the equation for the electric field strength due to a point charge, $E = \dfrac{q}{4\pi\varepsilon_0 r^2} = k\dfrac{q}{r^2}$;

5.3.7 Understand that for a uniform electric field, the field strength is constant, and recall and use the equation $E = \dfrac{V}{d}$

5.3.8 Recognise similarities and differences in gravitational and electric fields.

Electric Charges and Coulomb's Law

The diagram opposite shows the electric fields created by two electric charges q_1 and q_2. Each experiences a force since they are within the electric field created by the other charge.

Coulomb's Law states that between every two point charges there exists an electrical force which is directly proportional to the charge of each and is inversely proportional to the square of their separation.

This is written mathematically as:

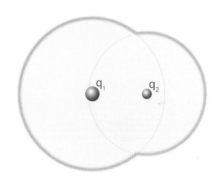

$F = k\dfrac{q_1 q_2}{r^2}$ where the constant $k = \dfrac{1}{4\pi\varepsilon_0}$

The value of the constant, k, depends on the nature of the material which is present between the point charges. This constant can be found experimentally. For charges in a vacuum, the constant k is 8.99×10^9 Nm² C⁻². The constant ε_0 shown above is known as the **permittivity of a vacuum**.

Unlike the force between point masses, the force between electrical charges may be attractive or repulsive. The force is **attractive** when the charges have **different** signs. The force is **repulsive** when the charges have the **same** sign.

Electric Field Strength

The electric field strength at a point in an electric field is the force on a charge of 1 coulomb placed at that point.

The symbol for electric field strength is a vector and it has the units NC⁻¹. As you will see later, an alternative unit is Vm⁻¹. The symbol for electric field strength is E. The direction of the electric field at a given point is the direction in which a positive electric charge would experience a force when placed at that point. The diagrams below show the electric fields around a variety of electric charges.

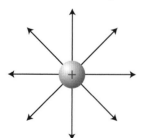

Isolated positive charge

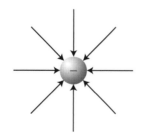

Isolated negative charge

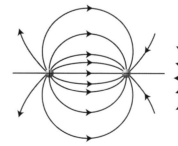

Equal positive and negative charges

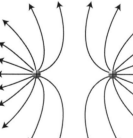

Two equal positive charges

The table below summarises the differences and similarities between gravitational and electric fields.

	Gravitational Fields	Electric Fields
Differences	• Acts on masses • Always produces an attractive force on a mass • Impossible to shield an object from a gravitational field	• Acts on charges • Can produce both attractive and repulsive forces because there are two types of charge (positive and negative) • Shielding is possible with a suitable material.
Similarities	• Field around a point mass decreases according to an inverse square law (falls off as $1/r^2$) • Field is of infinite range	• Field around a point charge decreases according to an inverse square law (falls off as $1/r^2$) • Field is of infinite range

The Uniform Electric Field

A uniform electric field has the same field strength throughout. Such a field can be created using a pair of parallel metal plates, a distance d apart, with a constant potential difference V between them, as shown in the diagram.

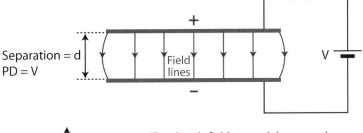

The electric field strength for this uniform field is given by:

$$E = \frac{V}{d} \text{ with unit } Vm^{-1}$$

The graph opposite shows how the electric potential varies with distance from the upper (positive) metal plate to the lower (negative) one.

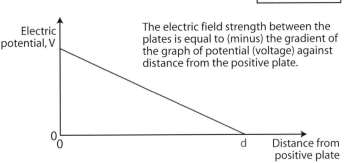

The electric field strength between the plates is equal to (minus) the gradient of the graph of potential (voltage) against distance from the positive plate.

Worked Example

(a) Define electric field strength.

(b) (i) According to the Bohr model of hydrogen, an electron in its ground state will orbit the nucleus with a radius of 5.29×10^{-13} m. Given that the nucleus of hydrogen consists of a single proton, calculate the electric field strength due to the proton at this radius. The proton may be taken to be a point charge.

(ii) Calculate the magnitude of the force between the electron and the proton when the electron is in its ground state. State whether the force is attractive or repulsive and explain your answer. (CCEA AY221 Summer 2011)

(a) The force acting on a charge of 1 coulomb at a point in an electric field.

(b) (i) The electric field strength is given by $E = k\dfrac{q}{r^2}$

The charge q is the charge on the proton $= 1.6\times10^{-19}$ C (from data sheet)

Substitution of values gives $E = \dfrac{8.99\times10^9 \times 1.6\times10^{-19}}{(5.29\times10^{-13})^2}$

$E = 5.14\times10^{15}$ NC^{-1}.

(ii) The electric force = electric field strength × the charge

$= 5.14\times10^{15} \times 1.6\times10^{-19}$

$= 8.22\times10^{-4}$ N

The force is attractive since the proton is positive and the electron is negative, and unlike charges attract.

Exercise 12

1. (a) State Coulomb's Law for the force F between two point charges.

(b) A point charge q_1 of charge 5 µC is suspended by a thread of length 0.60 m from a point A and hangs in position B. A second point charge q_2 of charge −3 µC is brought to, and held at, point D. As shown in the diagram, charge q_1 will move under the influence of the second charge q_2 to an equilibrium position at the point C.

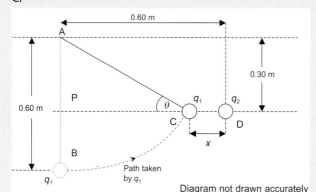

Diagram not drawn accurately

(i) Draw the force diagram (free–body diagram) for the point charge in the equilibrium position C. Label all the forces you have drawn.

(ii) The distance CD is 0.08 m. Calculate the electrostatic force acting on charge q_1 due to charge q_2 when q_1 is in position C.

(iii) The thread hangs at an angle of 30° to the horizontal. Calculate the tension in the string.

(CCEA AY221 Summer 2010 modified)

2. (a) (i) What is meant by a **field of force**?

(ii) State one similarity and one difference between electric and gravitational fields:

(b) A sphere of mass 2.30 g has an electric charge of +3.40 µC. It is dropped in a vacuum between two metal plates as shown in the diagram.

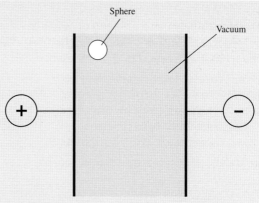

The plates are separated by 9.0 cm, and a potential difference of 160 V is applied between them.

(i) Calculate the magnitude of the gravitational force acting on the sphere.

(ii) Calculate the magnitude of the electrical force acting on the sphere.

(CCEA A2Y21 January 2010 legacy modified)

3. The diagram shows two point charges Q_1 and Q_2 of magnitude +2 µC and +4.5 µC respectively placed a distance 20 cm apart.

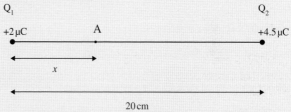

The resultant electric field strength at A, a distance x from Q_1, due to the charges Q_1 and Q_2 is zero.

(a) Calculate the magnitude of x.

(b) A charge of +3 µC is now placed at the point A. State the value of the electric force exerted on the +3 µC charge at A and explain your answer.

(CCEA A2Y21 Summer 2009 legacy modified)

5.4 Capacitors

Students should be able to:

5.4.1 Define capacitance;

5.4.2 Recall and use the equation $C = \dfrac{Q}{V}$;

5.4.3 Define the unit of capacitance, the farad;

5.4.4 Recall and use ½QV for calculating the energy of a charged capacitor;

5.4.5 Use the equations for the equivalent capacitance for capacitors in series and in parallel;

5.4.6 Describe experiments to demonstrate the charge and discharge of a capacitor;

5.4.7 Explain exponential decay using discharge curves;

5.4.8 Define time constant and use the equation $\tau = CR$;

5.4.9 Describe an experiment to determine the time constant for R–C circuits;

5.4.10 Apply knowledge and understanding of time constants and stored energy to electronic flash guns;

A capacitor is an electrical component that can store energy in the electric field between a pair of metal plates separated by an insulator, as shown in the diagram. The symbol for a capacitor is also shown.

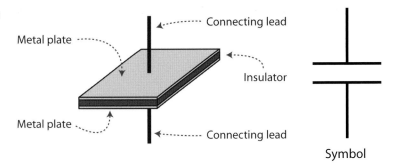

Charging is the process of storing energy in the capacitor and involves electric charges of equal magnitude, but opposite polarity, building up on each plate. A capacitor's ability to store charge is measured by its **capacitance**, in units of **farads, F**.

Capacitance is defined as the charge stored per volt.

The farad is a very large unit and microfarads (μF) and picofarads (pF) are more common.

$1 \mu F = 1.0 \times 10^{-6}$ F and $1 pF = 1.0 \times 10^{-12}$ F

Capacitance is calculated using this equation:

$C = \dfrac{Q}{V}$ where C = the capacitance in Farads, F

Q = the charge in Coulombs, C

V = the potential difference in Volts, V

This relationship can be shown by plotting a graph of Q (vertical axis) and V (horizontal axis). The result is a straight line through the origin, where the gradient is the capacitance.

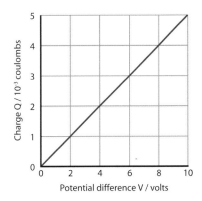

Capacitors in Parallel

In the circuit shown, the total charge stored is:

$Q_1 + Q_2 + Q_3$

The effective or total capacitance of the circuit C is given by:

$C = C_1 + C_2 + C_3$

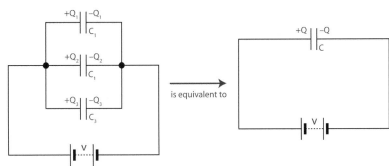

is equivalent to

Capacitors in Series

The total charge stored in this circuit is Q, not 3Q.

The effective or total capacitance of the circuit C is given by:

$\dfrac{1}{C} = \dfrac{1}{C_1} + \dfrac{1}{C_2} + \dfrac{1}{C_3}$

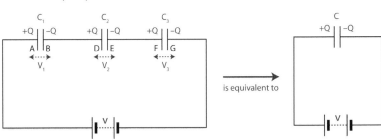

is equivalent to

Worked Example

(a) Two capacitors of capacitance 16 μF and 8μF are connected in parallel. Find their total capacitance.

(b) The two capacitors are now connected in series. Find their new total capacitance.

(a) Total capacitance $C = C_1 + C_2 = 16 + 8 = 24$ μF

(b) Using $\dfrac{1}{C} = \dfrac{1}{C_1} + \dfrac{1}{C_2} = \dfrac{1}{16} + \dfrac{1}{8} = \dfrac{3}{16}$

So $\dfrac{1}{C} = \dfrac{3}{16}$ therefore $C = \dfrac{16}{3} = 5.33$ μF (to 3 significant figures)

Energy of a Charged Capacitor

The energy E stored by a capacitor is given by: $E = \frac{1}{2} QV$

Using the relationship $C = \dfrac{Q}{V}$ alternative equations can be derived for the energy:

$$E = \tfrac{1}{2} CV^2$$

$$E = \dfrac{Q^2}{2C}$$

The graphs shown below are examples for a capacitor of value 6800mF.

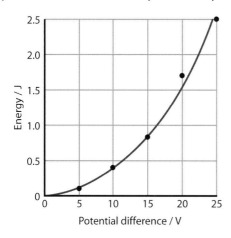

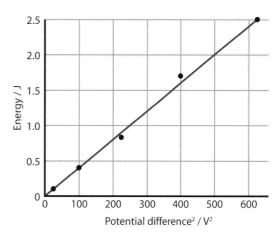

Note carefully

The equation $E = \frac{1}{2} QV$ might suggest that the energy is proportional to V. This is not the case. Remember that as V increases so does Q. The equation $E = \frac{1}{2} CV^2$ shows that the energy is actually proportional to V^2, since the capacitance C is constant for a given capacitor. The graphs above demonstrate this to be true.

Charging a Capacitor

The circuit shows a capacitor connected in series with a battery, a switch and a resistor. When the switch is closed the capacitor charges. Electrons flow onto one plate, which causes electrons to be repelled from the other plate. This movement of electrons constitutes a current.

Initially there are no electrons on the negative plate, so the rate of flow of electrons (current) is therefore large.

This falls off gradually as the repulsive effect of the electrons increases.

As the first graph shows, the resistance in the circuit also has an effect on how rapidly the charging current decreases.

As the capacitor stores an increasing amount of charge so the potential difference across it also increases, as shown in the second graph. Eventually this potential difference reaches the e.m.f. of the charging battery and at this point the flow of electrons ceases.

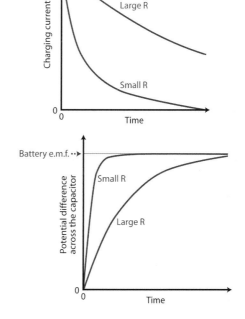

Discharging a Capacitor

The circuit opposite can be used to investigate the discharge of a capacitor. When the switch is moved to position A the capacitor is charged from the battery. The capacitor becomes fully charged very quickly since the resistance of the charging circuit is very small. Moving the switch to position B will start the capacitor discharging through the resistor R.

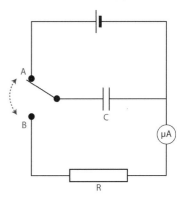

The current will begin high and gradually decrease, as shown in the first graph. This is an exponential decrease and described by the equation:

$$I = I_0 e^{\frac{-t}{\tau}}$$ where: I_0 = the initial current in A

I = the current after a time, t, in A

t = the time in s

τ = the time constant

The time constant τ is the time take for the current to fall to $\frac{1}{e}$ or 0.37 of its initial value. After a time equal to 2τ the current will 0.37 of 0.37, ie 0.137 of its initial value. The second graph shows this relationship. The time constant is calculated by the equation:

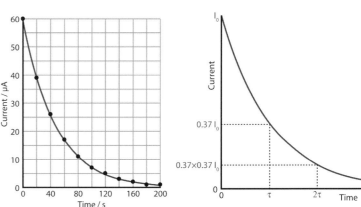

$\tau = CR$ where: C = the capacitance in F

R = the resistance in Ω

The product of capacitance and resistance has the unit of time and you can show this as follows:

$$C = \frac{Q}{V} \text{ and } R = \frac{V}{I} \text{ so therefore } CR = \frac{Q}{V} \times \frac{V}{I} = \frac{Q}{I}$$

However, current = charge × time, so $Q = It$

Therefore $CR = \frac{It}{I} = t$ (time)

Worked Example

A R-C circuit has a capacitance of 470 µF and resistance of 100 kΩ. Calculate the time constant.

$C = 4.7 \times 10^{-4}$ F and $R = 1 \times 10^5$ Ω

Using $\tau = CR = 4.7 \times 10^{-4} \times 1 \times 10^5 = 47$ s (seconds)

The voltage V across the capacitor and the charge Q on the capacitor also decrease exponentially when it is discharged. The equations below describe each of these decreases.

$$Q = Q_0 e^{\frac{-t}{\tau}}$$ where: Q_0 = the initial current in A

Q = the current after a time, t, in A

t = the time in s

τ = the time constant

$$V = V_0 e^{\frac{-t}{\tau}}$$ where: Q_0 = the initial current in A

Q = the current after a time, t, in A

t = the time in s

τ = the time constant

Measuring the Time Constant for a R-C circuit

A circuit for investigating the discharge of a capacitor has already been discussed. Values of current against time can be plotted directly and a exponential decay curve plotted. The time constant is the time for the current to fall to $\frac{1}{e}$ or 0.37 of its initial value. Drawing curves by hand is difficult and a better method is to obtain a straight line graph.

Plotting a graph of **ln I** on the y-axis and **time t** on the x-axis gives a straight line as shown on the right. The gradient of the line will give the value of the time constant τ.

Since τ = CR if either the capacitance or the resistance is known, the other can be found.

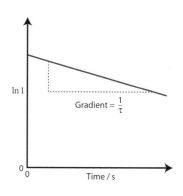

Worked Example

The diagram shows a circuit which can be used to charge a capacitor C of capacitance 6 µF. The switch S_1 is closed at time t = 0.

(a) Sketch a graph to show how the voltage V, recorded by the voltmeter varies with time t during the charging of the capacitor.

Label each axis and label the final value for V on the y-axis.

(b) Explain how the movement of charge carriers in the circuit, after the switch is closed, can explain the shape of the graph you have drawn.

(c) The switch is now moved to position S_2 and the capacitor discharges through resistor R. After 48 seconds, the voltage has fallen from 12.0 V to 1.64 V. Use these data to calculate the size of resistance R.
(CCEA AY221 Summer 2010 modified)

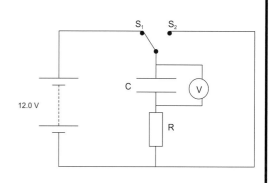

(a) The voltage increases from zero. The rate of increase decreases with time. See graph opposite.

(b) Initially, there is a rapid flow of charge electrons because the capacitor is uncharged. As the number of electrons increases the force repelling further electrons increases. This slows the increase in the voltage and charge being stored on the plates of the capacitor.

(c) *There are two methods you can use.*

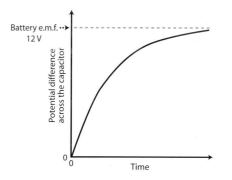

Firstly, divide voltage at time t = 48 s by the initial voltage:
1.64 ÷ 12 = 0.137 This equals 0.37 × 0.37.
This means 48s is two time constants.
Therefore 2τ = 48 s so τ = 24 s

Secondly, use $V = V_0 \, e^{\frac{-t}{\tau}}$
$1.67 = 12 \, e^{\frac{-48}{\tau}}$ so $0.137 = e^{\frac{-48}{\tau}}$

Taking natural logs of both sides gives:
$-1.99 = \dfrac{-48}{\tau}$ so $\tau = \dfrac{48}{1.99} = 24$ s

---

Uses of Capacitors

Defibrillators deliver a carefully controlled shock to a heart attack victim, whose heart muscles are twitching in an uncoordinated fashion known as ventricular fibrillation. The controlled shock is designed to stop the fibrillation and start the normal heart rhythm again. A defibrillator needs to transfer a precise amount of energy to a patient. The best way to do this is to use a capacitor. The capacitor stores electric charge on its plates. The energy that it stores is in the form of the electric field that is created between its plates. This energy is delivered as a pulse lasting just a few milliseconds.

Electronic flash guns use an electric discharge in a suitable gas such as xenon to produce an intense flash of light that lasts a short time. In the case of a flash gun used with a camera, it must be operated from a small battery, say, 6V. To achieve the flash, electronic circuitry has to be used to generate a high voltage, ie several hundred volts. When the shutter on the camera is pressed the charged capacitor is rapidly discharged through the gas-filled flash tube so producing the intense flash of light.

Exercise 13

1. Two capacitors, C_1 of capacitance 2.00 μF and C_2 of capacitance of 8.00 μF are charged so that the energy stored in **each** capacitor is 5.76×10^{-4} J. This energy remains stored in the capacitors as they are connected in the circuit shown with switch S open.

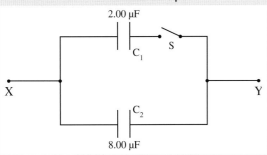

(a) Calculate the potential difference across each of the capacitors. Reminder: the switch is open at this stage.

(b) Switch S is now closed.
    (i) Find the potential difference between the terminals X and Y after the switch is closed.
    (ii) Describe and explain the transfer of charge between the capacitors after the switch is closed.
(CCEA A2Y21 Summer 2009 legacy modified)

2. (a) A capacitor of capacitance C is connected to a supply voltage which is gradually increased from zero to a value V_{max}.
    (i) At a particular instant, the potential difference across the capacitor is V_1. Write down an expression, in terms of C and V_1, for the energy E_1 stored in the capacitor at that instant.
    (ii) Sketch a graph to show how the energy E stored in the capacitor depends on the supply voltage V up to the maximum of V_{max}.

(iii) The capacitance of the capacitor is 10.0 μF. Over a period of time, as a result of changing the supply voltage, the charge on the capacitor is increased from 30.0 μC to 90.0 μC. Calculate the range of supply voltage that produces this change in charge.

(b) (i) A capacitor has capacitance C and carries a charge Q. Write down an expression, in terms of C and Q, for the energy E stored in the capacitor.
    (ii) The circuit diagram shows three capacitors connected in series to a battery.

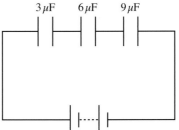

Which of the capacitors has the least energy stored in it? Explain your reasoning.
(CCEA A2Y21 January 2010 legacy modified)

3. (a) The time constant of a resistor–capacitor (R–C) circuit is numerically equal to the product of the resistance and the capacitance in the circuit. Draw a circuit diagram that will enable the time constant of a resistor–capacitor network to be determined.

(b) (i) Describe how the circuit is used to obtain results from which the time constant may be determined. You should name any additional equipment required.
    (ii) Explain how the results from (b)(i) are analysed to obtain a value for the time constant.

(CCEA AY221 June 2011 modified)

5.5 Magnetic Fields

Students should be able to:

5.5.1 Explain the concept of a magnetic field;

5.5.2 Understand that there is a force on a current–carrying conductor in a perpendicular magnetic field and be able to predict the direction of the force;

5.5.3 Define magnetic flux density using the equation $F = BIl$

5.5.4 Define the unit of magnetic flux density, the tesla;

5.5.5 Understand the concepts of magnetic flux and magnetic flux linkage;

5.5.6 Recall and use the equations for magnetic flux, $\Phi = BA$, and magnetic flux linkage $N\Phi = BAN$

5.5.7 Define the unit of magnetic flux, the weber;

5.5.8 State, use and demonstrate experimentally Faraday's and Lenz's laws of electromagnetic induction;

5.5.9 Recall and calculate induced e.m.f. as rate of change of flux linkage with time;

5.5.10 Describe how a transformer works;

5.5.11 Recall and use the equation $\dfrac{V_s}{V_p} = \dfrac{N_s}{N_p} = \dfrac{I_p}{I_s}$ for transformers.

5.5.12 Explain power losses in transformers and the advantages of high voltage transmission of electricity.

The space surrounding a magnet where a magnetic force is experienced is called a **magnetic field**. The direction of a magnetic field at a point is taken as the direction of the force that acts on a north pole placed at that point. The shape of a magnetic field can be represented by a magnetic field lines. Arrows on the lines show the direction of the magnetic field. The direction of a magnetic field on a permanent magnet is from North to South, as shown below (left).

A magnetic field also surrounds a conductor carrying an electrical current. Around a straight wire, the field lines form concentric circles as shown below (right). The direction can be obtained by using the right hand screw rule. If a right handed screw moves forward in the same direction as the current, then the direction of rotation of the screw gives the direction of the magnetic field lines.

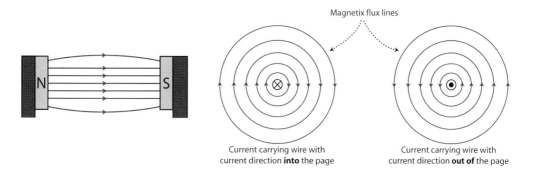

Magnetix flux lines

Current carrying wire with current direction **into** the page

Current carrying wire with current direction **out of** the page

When a current flows through a conductor which is placed in a magnetic field, the conductor experiences a force.

The diagram on the right shows a flexible wire in a magnetic field. When a current is passed along the flexible wire, the wire moves up. The force acts at right angles to both the current and the magnetic field direction.

The direction of the force (movement) of the wire is obtained from Fleming's Left Hand Rule, which is shown on the far right.

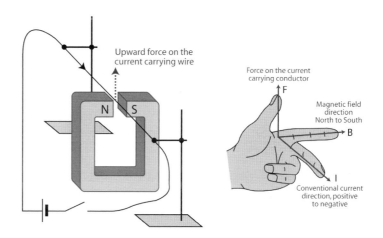

Upward force on the current carrying wire

Force on the current carrying conductor

F

Magnetic field direction North to South

B

Conventional current direction, positive to negative

This force arises because of the interaction of the two magnetic fields: the uniform field of the permanent magnet and the field due to the current in the wire. The magnetic field lines of force are vectors and the field lines due to two fields have to be combined vectorially, as shown on the right.

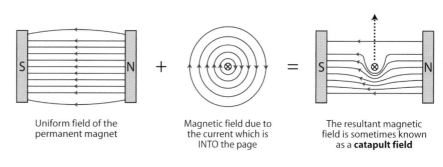

Uniform field of the permanent magnet

Magnetic field due to the current which is INTO the page

The resultant magnetic field is sometimes known as a **catapult field**

In the case when the magnetic field and the current are at right angles the force is given by:

$F = BIl$ where: B = the magnetic flux density in tesla, T

I = the current in the conductor in A

l = the length of the conductor in the magnetic field in m

Re–arranging the above equation allows us to give a definition of mangnetic flux density and the unit tesla.

$$B = \frac{FI}{l}$$

Magnetic flux density is therefore the force per unit current carrying length. The definition of the Tesla is therefore:
A magnetic field of flux density 1.0 T will exert a force of 1.0 N on a current carrying length of 1.0 Am.

A 'current carrying length' is the product of current and length. For example, a current of 0.25 A in a wire of length 0.4 m is a current carrying length of $0.25 \times 0.4 = 0.1$ Am.

Verification of F = BI*l*

The apparatus shown on the right can be used to investigate how the force acting on a current carrying conductor depends on the current flowing in the conductor and the length of the conductor in the magnetic field. An aluminium rod is clamped horizontally above a sensitive electronic balance. The rod is connected to a variable low voltage supply. An ammeter connected in series with both will allow the current to be measured.

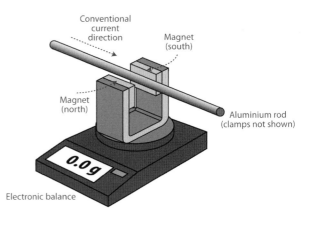

A permanent magnet is placed on the balance and the aluminium rod positioned so that it is located in the centre of the magnetic field. The balance is set to read zero after the magnets have been placed on it. When a current is then passed along the clamped aluminium rod the rod experiences a force due to the interaction of the permanent magnetic field and the magnetic field due to the current in the aluminium rod. In the case shown in the diagram, the force is upwards. Use Fleming's Left Hand Rule to verify this.

The current is varied with a single magnet in place. This ensures that the length of the conductor in the magnetic field remains constant.

A graph of the force (y-axis) against current (x-axis) produces a straight line through the origin, as shown in the first graph. This is verification that the force on the current carrying conductor in the magnetic field is directly proportional to the current.

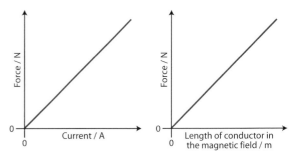

The current is then fixed and a number of identical magnets are placed side by side. This changes the length of the conductor in the magnetic field. A graph of force (y-axis) against the length of conductor in the magnetic field (x-axis) produces a straight line through the origin, as shown in the second graph. This is verification that the force on the current carrying conductor in the magnetic field is directly proportional to the length of the conductor in the magnetic field.

Worked Example

A straight wire of length 50 cm carries a current of 1.75 A. Calculate the value of the force that acts on this wire when a length of 30 cm of this wire is placed at right angles to a magnetic field of flux density 5.5×10⁻² T.

Use F = BI*l*

Note that only 30 cm of the wire is in the magnetic field, so *l* = 0.30 m

$F = BIl = 5.5 \times 10^{-2} \times 1.75 \times 0.30 = 0.029 \text{ N}$

Magnetic Flux Φ

Magnetic flux lines (magnetic field lines) show the direction of a magnetic field. Their spacing indicates the strength of the field, the closer the field lines, the stronger the magnetic field. Magnetic flux, Φ, represents the total number of magnetic flux lines that pass at 90° through a given area. Magnetic flux is measured in webers (Wb) and is given by:

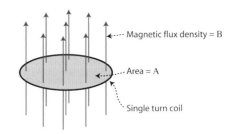

$\Phi = BA$ where: Φ = the magnetic flux in Wb

$\qquad$ B = the magnetic flux density, perpendicular to the plane of the coil, in T

$\qquad$ A = the area in m²

Magnetic flux linkage NΦ

Magnetic flux linkage is used when calculating the total magnetic flux passing through or linking a coil of N turns and area of cross section A. Magnetic flux linkage is also measured in webers (Wb), since N does not have a unit.

$N\Phi = BAN$ where: Φ = the magnetic flux in Wb

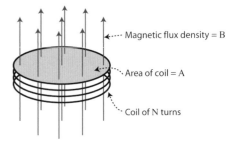

$\qquad$ B = the magnetic flux density, perpendicular to the plane of the coil, in T

$\qquad$ A = the area in m²

$\qquad$ N = the number of turns in the coil

Worked Example

(a) A coil of 200 turns, each of diameter 5 cm, is placed in a uniform magnetic field of flux density 0.5 T. The magnetic field direction is perpendicular to the plane of the coil. Calculate the magnetic flux linkage.
(b) The coil is now rotated so that the magnetic field direction makes an angle of 30° with the normal to the plane of the coil. Calculate the new magnetic flux linkage in the coil.

(a) Use $N\Phi = BAN$
    Area $A = \pi r^2 = \pi \times 5^2 = 78.5$ cm^2 $= 7.85\times10^{-3}$ m^2
    So $N\Phi = BAN = 0.5 \times 7.85\times10^{-3} \times 200 = 0.785$ Wb

(b) Only the perpendicular component of the magnetic flux density, $B_\perp$ passes through the coil.
    $B_\perp = B \cos 30 = 0.5 \cos 30 = 0.5 \times 0.866 = 0.433$ T
    So new $N\Phi = B_\perp AN = 0.433 \times 7.85\times10^{-3} \times 200 = 0.680$ Wb

Exercise 14

1. A wire is suspended in a magnetic field between two identical magnets as shown in the diagram below. The north pole of each magnet is shaded. The wire is suspended so that it cannot move. The magnets are placed on electronic scales. The wire is attached to a variable power supply and ammeter. The reading on the scales is adjusted to zero.

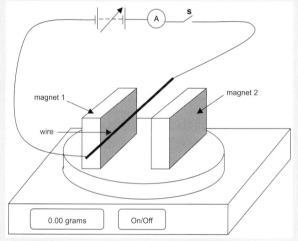

(a) (i) The switch S is closed. In what direction does the wire experience a force?
(ii) By considering Newton's Third Law, state and explain the effect of this force on the reading on the electronic scales.

(b) The change in the scale reading from 0.00g when different currents were passed through the wire is shown in the table below.

Current/A	Change in the scale reading/g	
	Reading 1	Reading 2
1.37	0.35	– 0.35
3.67	0.94	– 0.92
4.99	1.28	– 1.28
6.38	1.63	– 1.64

(i) Explain how it is possible to obtain two scale readings for each current, one positive and the other negative.
(ii) Using the values from Reading 1 plot a suitable graph to allow you to find the force produced by a current of 4.00 A.
(iii) The length of the wire in the magnetic field was 0.12 m. Calculate the magnetic flux density between the two magnets.

(CCEA AY221 Summer 2011 modified)

Electromagnetic Induction

An **e.m.f.** (electromotive force) can be induced in a coil of wire by moving a magnet towards or away from the coil or by moving a wire so that it cuts across the magnetic lines of flux. For an e.m.f. there must be relative motion between the magnet and the conductor, the wire or coil of wire.

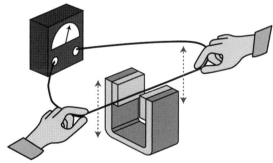 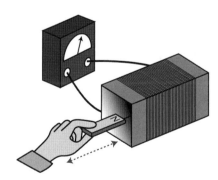

The magnitude of the e.m.f. is proportional to:
• the strength of the magnet
• the number of turns on the coil
• the speed of the moving magnet

Faraday's Law of Electromagnetic Induction states:
The magnitude of the induced e.m.f. is equal to the rate of change of magnetic flux linkage.

The direction of the induced e.m.f. depends on the direction in which the magnet is moving and on the type of magnetic pole nearest the coil. We can demonstrate this using the simple apparatus shown overleaf.

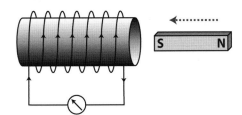 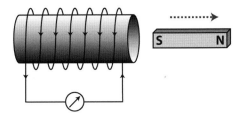

Moving the south pole of the magnet towards the coil causes the induced current to flow so that it creates a south magnetic pole in the coil opposing the incoming south pole of the magnet. Work has to be done against this opposing force.	Moving the south pole of the magnet away from the coil causes the induced current to reverse direction. It now flows so that it creates a north magnetic pole in the coil attracting the retreating pole of the magnet. Work again has to be done against this opposing force.

Lenz's Law of Electromagnetic Induction states:
The direction of the induced current is such that it opposes the change in the magnetic flux that is producing it.

Lenz's Law is the Principle of Conservation of Energy in action. The kinetic energy of the moving magnet is converted to electrical energy when work is done against the opposing force.

Calculation of Induced e.m.f.

Faraday's Law states that the size of the induced e.m.f. is equal to the rate of change of the number of magnetic field lines passing through the coil. It is given by:

$$E = = -\frac{\Delta N\Phi}{\Delta t}$$ where: E = e.m.f in volts, V

$\Delta N\Phi$ = change in the magnetic flux linkage in Wb

Δt = time during which the change in the magnetic flux linkage occurs, in s

Exercise 15

1. (a) (i) State Faraday's Law of Electromagnetic Induction.
(ii) Describe an experiment in which Faraday's law of electromagnetic induction can be demonstrated. Your answer should include; a labelled diagram of the apparatus and an explanation as to how the results or observations demonstrate Faraday's law.

(b) A loop of wire is placed in the magnetic field produced by an electromagnet. The loop of wire has a resistance of **2.6 Ω** and an area of **4.0×10⁻³ m²**. When the electromagnet is switched on it takes **0.8 s** to reach its maximum flux density of **600 µT**.

Assuming all the magnetic field lines pass through the loop, and the loop's area is perpendicular to the field, calculate the average current that flows in the wire during the 0.8 s after the electromagnet is switched on.

(CCEA AY221 Summer 2010 modified)

2. A flat coil of wire is placed with its plane perpendicular to a magnetic field. The flux Φ through the coil is initially constant, but changes with time t as shown in the diagram.

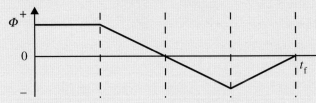

Copy the graph and on it draw another graph to show how the induced e.m.f. in the coil changes with time t from t = 0 to t = t_f.

(CCEA A2Y21 Summer 2009 legacy modified)

The Transformer

The principle of the transformer can be demonstrated using two coils arranged as shown in the diagram opposite. When the switch of coil 1 is closed the meter gives a momentary deflection to the right, and then goes back to zero.

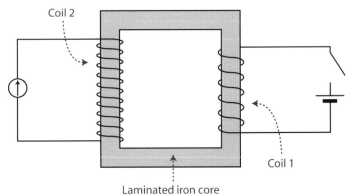

Laminated iron core

Closing the switch completes the circuit of coil 1, a current flows and a magnetic field quickly develops. The iron core ensures that magnetic flux lines link the turns of coil 2. This change in the magnetic flux linkage causes an e.m.f. to be induced in coil 2.

When the current in coil 1 reaches its final steady value, the magnetic field around it is steady, so the flux linkage is no longer changing and so there is no induced e.m.f. When the switch is opened the current in coil 1 falls, and its magnetic field decreases. The magnetic flux linkage through coil 2 decreases and e.m.f. is induced again, but in the opposite direction to the first one.

Transformers convert alternating current at one voltage to alternating current at a different voltage.

The diagram shows the structure of a typical transformer. In practice, for increased efficiency, the coils are wound on top of each other. They are shown separated here for clarity.

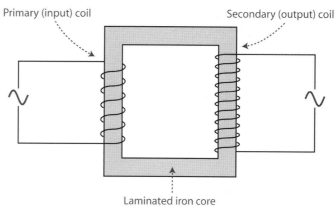

An alternating current in the primary coil produces an alternating magnetic field, a field whose strength varies continuously and whose direction reverses periodically.

This changing magnetic field causes the magnetic flux linking the secondary coil to change so an e.m.f. is induced in the secondary coil. The iron core maximises the magnetic flux linking both coils.

The ratio of the turns on each coil determines the ratio of the two voltages, ie:

$$\frac{N_s}{N_p} = \frac{V_s}{V_p}$$

where: N_p = the number of turns on the primary (input) coil
N_s = the number of turns on the secondary (output) coil
V_p = the voltage applied to the primary (input) coil
V_s = the voltage developed across the secondary (output) coil

If we assume that the efficiency of the transformer is 1 then we can write:

Input power = Output power

or $\quad I_p \times V_p = I_s \times V_s$

or $\quad \dfrac{V_s}{V_p} = \dfrac{I_p}{I_s}$ $\quad$ Note carefully the different positions of the P and S on each side of this equation

Power Losses in a Transformer

The efficiency of real transformers is less than 1 (100%), ie not all of the input electrical energy appears as useful output electrical energy. Some of the various ways in which energy is wasted are described below:

1. Transformers have resistive heat losses due to the wires in the coils.

2. Not all of the magnetic flux of the primary passes through or links the secondary coil.

3. Repeatedly magnetising the iron core in one direction and then reversing the direction of magnetisation results in heating of the iron core.

4. The changing magnetic field induces large currents in the iron core. These are called eddy currents and are very large. They result in heating of the core. These eddy current are reduced by laminating the core.

Transmission of Electricity

Transformers play an important role in the transmission of electricity from the generating stations to the consumers. At the generating end they step the voltage up before it is connected to the transmission cables and at the consumer end they step the voltage down for use in appliances.

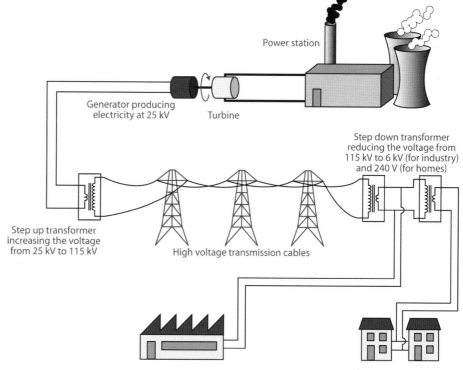

Advantages of High Voltage Electricity Transmission

The cables used to transmit the electrical power from the generator to the consumer have resistance. This means energy is lost as heat due to resistive heating. The diagram is a simplified picture of the electricity generation and transmission system.

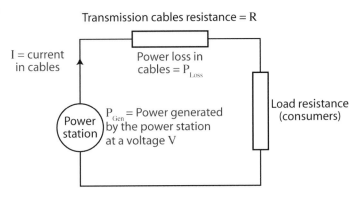

Transmission cables resistance = R

I = current in cables

Power loss in cables = P_{Loss}

Load resistance (consumers)

P_{Gen} = Power generated by the power station at a voltage V

Power station

The power generated is P_{Gen}.

The resistance, R, is constant.

The power loss in the cables $P_{Loss} = I^2R$.

$P_{Gen} = IV$ therefore $I = \dfrac{P_{Gen}}{V}$ and $P_{Loss} = \dfrac{P_{Gen}^2 R}{V^2}$

Since P_{Gen} and R are both constants this shows that the power loss in the cables P_{Loss} is inversely proportional to the square of the voltage at which the electricity is transmitted to the consumer, ie if the voltage is doubled the power loss is reduced by a factor of four, and the current I is reduced by a factor of two.

One way to reduce the power loss in electricity cables would be to make the resistance of the cables smaller by using cables of a very large cross section area. However, this would considerably increase their weight and the cost.

The other way is to reduce the current. This is the function of the step up transformer at the generating station. The voltage is stepped up and the current is reduced. The electrical power is then transmitted at a high voltage and a low current, which considerably reduces the energy loss. The advantage of this is demonstrated by the following example:

Worked Example

A power station generates 400 MW of electrical power at a voltage of 25 kV.
The transmission lines have a resistance of 0.25 Ω per kilometre.
(a) Calculate the energy loss if the power is transmitted at 25 kV.
(b) Calculate the energy loss if a transformer is used to step up the voltage to 115 kV before it is transmitted.

(a) Current $I = \dfrac{P}{V} = \dfrac{400 \times 10^6}{25 \times 10^3} = 1.6 \times 10^4$ A

So power loss $P_{Loss} = I^2R = (1.6 \times 10^4)^2 \times 0.25 = 6.4 \times 10^7$ W $= 64$ MW per km

(a) Current $I = \dfrac{P}{V} = \dfrac{400 \times 10^6}{115 \times 10^3} = 3.48 \times 10^3$ A

So power loss $P_{Loss} = I^2R = (3.48 \times 10^3)^2 \times 0.25 = 3.03 \times 10^6$ W $= 3.03$ MW per km

---

Exercise 16

1. Transformers are used to change the value of an alternating voltage. The diagram illustrates part of the structure of a transformer. In the actual transformer the coils would be wound tightly around the laminated iron core and there would be leads to the primary coil and leads from the secondary coil. The coils are made from insulated copper wire.

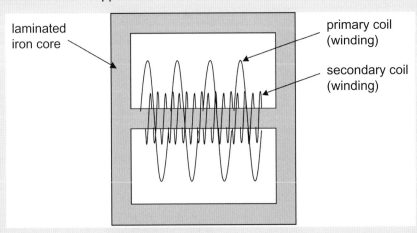

laminated iron core

primary coil (winding)

secondary coil (winding)

(a) Transformers of this design have an efficiency of 97%. Explain how the transformer described above minimises energy losses.

(b)(i) The primary coil of this transformer, with 500 turns, is connected to a 230 V a.c. supply. Show that the emf induced in the 2800 turns of the secondary coil is 1.29 kV.

(ii) The 2800 turns of the secondary coil are would on the laminated iron core which as a cross–sectional area of 2.2×10^{-4} m². Calculate the change in the magnetic flux density every second to cause 1.29 kV to be induced in the secondary coil of this transformer.

(CCEA AY221 Summer 2011 modified)

2. (a) A transformer in a power supply for a portable CD player reduces the 240 V mains voltage to 6.0 V and delivers 2.0 W of power to the player.

(i) Calculate the ratio of the number of turns on the primary coil to the number on the secondary coil (i.e. the turns ratio).

(ii) Assuming the transformer to be 100% efficient calculate the current in the primary and secondary coils.

(b) Electrical power P is to be delivered at an output voltage V to a transmission system. The diagram below is a schematic of the system. The line resistance gives rise to a power loss X and the constant load resistance is R.

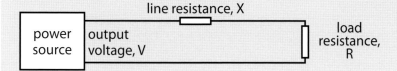

(i) Write down an expression for the current I in the system.
(ii) Show that, for a given power P delivered by the source, the power loss in the lines is inversely proportional to V^2, where V is the output voltage of the source.
(CCEA 1998 and 2000 modified)

5.6 Deflection of Charged Particles in Electric and Magnetic Fields

Students should be able to:

5.6.1 Understand that a moving charge in a uniform electric field experiences a force;

5.6.2 Recall and use the equation F = Eq to calculate the magnitude of the force on a charged particle in an electric field, and determine the direction of the force;

5.6.3 Understand that a moving charge in a uniform, perpendicular magnetic field experiences a force;

5.6.4 Recall and use the equation F = Bqv to calculate the magnitude of the force, and determine the direction of the force;

5.6.5 Outline the structure of the cathode ray oscilloscope;

5.6.6 Explain how the cathode ray oscilloscope can be used as a measuring instrument for voltage;

Energy Changes in an Electric Field

Cathode ray oscilloscopes, X-ray tubes and electron microscopes are all devices that use beams of electrons. The electrons come from a heated wire filament of an electron gun. When the wire is heated to a high temperature the electrons with sufficient energy escape from the surface of the filament by a process called thermionic emission.

The electrons emerge into an electric field created by a large potential difference between the cathode and the anode. The electrons are accelerated by this electric field. They lose electric potential energy and gain kinetic energy.

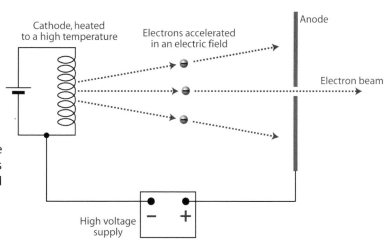

A volt is defined as a joule per coulomb, which means that a charge of 1 coulomb accelerated through a potential difference of 1 volt will gain 1 joule of energy. Using this definition, and applying the principle of conservation of energy we have:

Loss of electrical potential energy = Gain of kinetic energy

$eV = \frac{1}{2}m_e v^2$ where: V = potential difference between anode and cathode

  e = charge on the electron

  m_e = mass of the electron

  v = velocity of the electron

Other charged particles can be accelerated in a similar way. In this case, the equation above changes to account for the mass and charge of the particle:

$qV = \frac{1}{2}mv^2$ where: V = potential difference between anode and cathode

  q = charge on the particle

  m = mass of the particle

  v = velocity of the particle

Force on a Charged Particle in an Electric Field

The force on a charged particle in an electric field is given by:

$F = qE$ where: F = the force, in N

  q = charge, in C

  E = electric field strength in Vm^{-1} or NC^{-1}

The direction of an electric field is the direction in which a positive charge will experience a force when placed in the field (left diagram). Remember electrons have a **negative** charge so they will experience a force in a direction **opposite** to that of the electric field (right diagram).

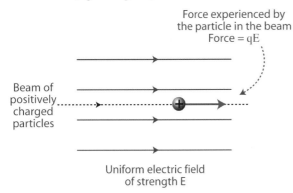

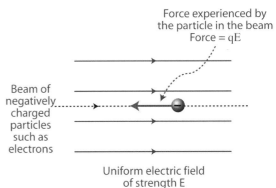

Worked Example

Positive ions, each of mass 7.75×10^{-27} kg and charge 3.50×10^{-19} C are accelerated in vacuum from rest to a speed of 4.25×10^4 ms^{-1}. Calculate the potential difference through which the ions are accelerated to give them this speed.

Using Loss of electrical potential energy = Gain of kinetic energy

$$\frac{1}{2}mv^2 = qV$$

So: $\frac{1}{2} \times 7.75 \times 10^{-27} \times (4.25 \times 10^4)^2 = 3.50 \times 10^{-19} \times V$

$7.00 \times 10^{-18} = 3.50 \times 10^{-19} \times V$

$V = 7.00 \times 10^{-18} \div 3.50 \times 10^{-19} = 20.0$ V

Deflection of Charged Particles in an Electric Field

The diagram shows what happens when a charged particle is projected into an electric field at right angles to the direction of the field. The charged particle experiences a force in the vertical direction only. So we treat its motion as a projectile, ie

• Horizontally motion: constant velocity

• Vertically motion: uniform acceleration from rest

The force on the charged particle is $F = qE$

Electric field strength is $E = \dfrac{V}{d}$

The acceleration $a = \dfrac{F}{m} = \dfrac{qV}{md}$

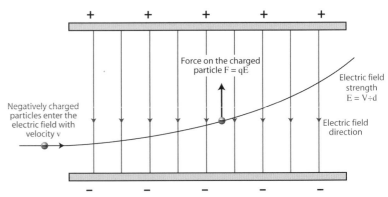

where: V = potential difference between the plates, in V

d = separation of the plates, in m

m = mass of the particle, in kg

The equations of motion can be applied to the motion of the charged particle as it moves through the electric field.

At time t = 0:

$v_x = v$

$v_y = 0$

At time t = t:

$v_x = v$

$v_y = \dfrac{qV}{md}t$

$x = vt$

$y = 0 + \dfrac{1}{2}at^2 = \dfrac{1}{2}\dfrac{qV}{md}t^2$

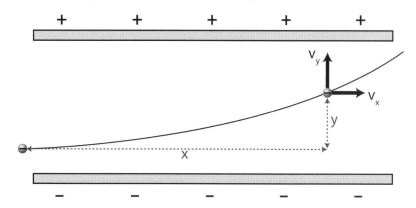

Worked Example

A plastic sphere of mass 7.82×10^{-14} kg carries a positive charge. It is held stationary between two parallel metal plates with a potential difference between them. This creates an electric field strength of magnitude 6.66×10^{4} Vm^{-1}.
(a) Draw a diagram to show the forces acting on the sphere.
(b) Calculate the charge on the sphere and the number of elementary charges carried by the sphere.
(CCEA AY221 January 2010 legacy modified)

(a) ↑ Electric force = qE

◯

↓ Weight = mg

(b) Since the sphere is stationary, we know that qE = mg

So: $q \times 6.66\times10^4 = 7.82\times10^{-14} \times 9.81$

$q = 1.52\times10^{-17}$ C

Then, to work out the number of elementry particles:

$q = Ne$, so $N = \dfrac{q}{e} = \dfrac{1.52\times10^{-17}}{1.6\times10^{-19}} = 95$ elementary charges

Deflection of Charged Particles in a Magnetic Field

A moving charge in a magnetic field experiences a force which is perpendicular to both the velocity of the particle and the direction of the magnetic field. Fleming's Left Hand Rule can be used to find the direction of this force, as shown in the diagram on the right.

Note carefully: To determine the direction of the force on an electron moving in a magnetic field you must remember that the movement of the electron is opposite to that of positive charge.

Since the force always acts at right angles to the velocity of the charged particles it causes the particles (electrons, protons, ions) to move in circular paths.

The diagrams below show the paths taken by beams of negatively charged and positively charged particles when they enter a magnetic field.

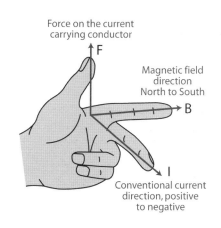

Force on the current carrying conductor

F

Magnetic field direction North to South

B

Conventional current direction, positive to negative

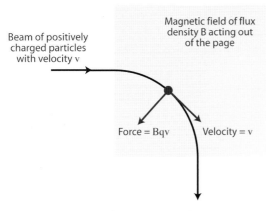

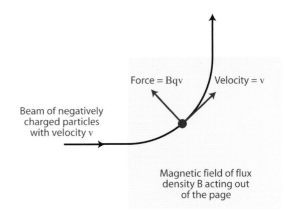

The force on the moving charge is given by:

$F = Bqv$ where: F = the force, in N

B = the magnetic field strength, in T

q = charge on the particle, in C

v = velocity of the particle, in ms^{-1}

Note: If the charged particles enter the magnetic field parallel or anti–parallel to the magnetic field lines they do **not** experience any force:

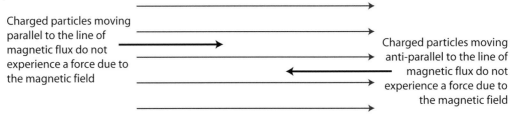

Charged particles moving parallel to the line of magnetic flux do not experience a force due to the magnetic field

Charged particles moving anti-parallel to the line of magnetic flux do not experience a force due to the magnetic field

Exercise 17

1. A proton enters the uniform electric field between two horizontal plates. It enters horizontally with a speed $v_o = 4.00 \times 10^5$ ms^{-1}.

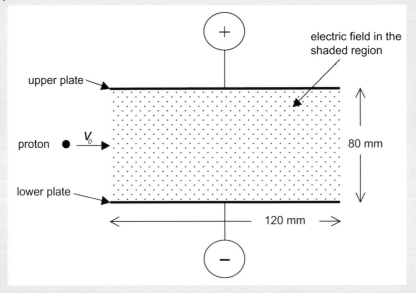

(a)(i) Calculate the magnitude of the electric field strength E if the voltage between the plates is 148 V.

(ii) Calculate the magnitude of the acceleration experienced by the proton if the electric field exerted a constant force of 2.96×10^{-16} N. The effect of gravity on the proton is negligible and can be ignored in this question.

(b) Calculate the magnitude and direction of the velocity of the proton on exiting the electric field. State the direction relative to the horizontal.

2. A beam of helium ions of mass m, charge q and travelling at a speed of v, enters a region EFGH at right angles as shown. The region EFGH is a square of side 8 cm and a uniform magnetic field of flux density B acts vertically out of the plane of the page throughout this region.

(a) (i) Explain why the helium ions follow a circular path when in the region EFGH.

(ii) Show that the radius r of the path taken by the ions while in the region EFGH is given by

$$r = \frac{mv}{Bq}$$

(iii) If the ions have a mass of 6.6×10^{-27} kg, a charge of 3.2×10^{-19} C and are travelling at a speed of 1.55×10^6 ms^{-1}, calculate the radius of the path of the ions if the magnetic field has a flux density of 0.80 T. Give your answer to the nearest cm.

(iv) Copy the diagram and sketch the path taken by the ions within region EFGH and show the direction they travel when they leave the region EFGH. Label this path P.

(b) The value of the magnetic flux density is increased to 1.60 T.

(i) Sketch the new path taken by the ions. Label this path Q.

(ii) Explain why the ions take this new path.

(CCEA AY221 Summer 2010 modified)

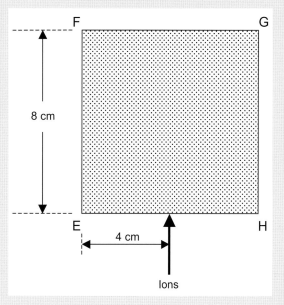

Cathode Ray Oscilloscope (CRO)

An oscilloscope is an instrument that allows voltages to be viewed as a graph with voltage on the vertical axis (y-axis) plotted as a function of time on the horizontal axis (x-axis). The oscilloscope can be used as a voltmeter to measure the size of a d.c. voltage and the amplitude of an a.c. voltage. It can also be used to measure time intervals and so allow the frequency of an alternating voltage to be determined.

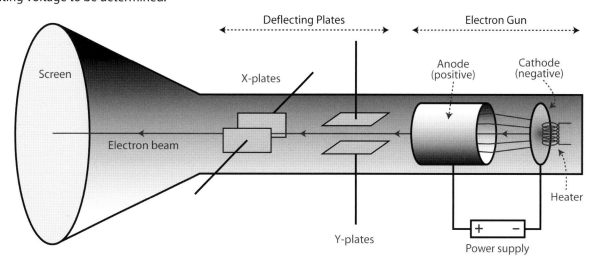

The pressure of gas inside the cathode ray tube is less than 0.01 Pa, one ten millionth of atmospheric pressure. Inside the cathode ray tube is a hot cathode which provides electrons and a series of electrodes which accelerate and focus the electrons into a narrow fast moving beam. This assembly is called the **electron gun**.

Along the path of the beam are **deflecting plates**. The Y plates deflect the beam in the vertical direction and the X plates deflect the beam in the horizontal direction. The layout of these components is shown in the diagram above.

The inside of the cathode ray tube at the screen end is coated with phosphor. When the electrons strike the screen, this phosphor is excited and light is emitted from that point. This conversion of the electron's kinetic energy into light allows us to see various traces and waveforms as points or lines of light on an otherwise darkened screen.

The voltage to be examined is usually applied to the Y plates. An internally generated voltage is applied to the x plates. Its function is to sweep the electron beam across the screen and then to quickly return it to the start and begin all over again. This is known as the **time base** and uses a sawtooth voltage as shown in the diagram below.

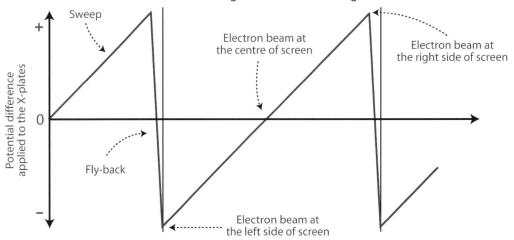

The display seen on the CRO screen depends on the type of voltage (a.c. or d.c) and on the whether the timebase is on or off. You can regard the screen of the CRO as a graph, the vertical scale (y-axis) is voltage and the horizontal scale (x-axis) time. The voltage scale (y-axis) can be changed and is usually marked in V/cm or mV/cm. The time scale (x-axis) can also be changed and this is marked in ms/cm or µs/cm.

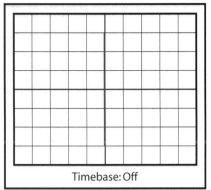

Timebase: Off

In this example, an a.c. voltage is applied to the y plates.

With the timebase OFF (left) the beam is deflected upwards and downwards.

In this example, the y-sensitivity is set to 100 mV/cm, so this represent a voltage that varies from +300 mV to −300 mV.

With the timebase ON (right) the CRO displays the waveform of the alternating voltage.

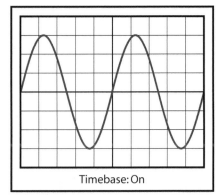

Timebase: On

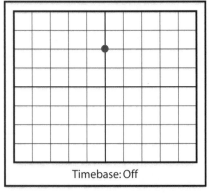

Timebase: Off

In this example, a +d.c. voltage is applied to the y plates.

With the timebase OFF (left) the beam is deflected upwards by 2 cm.

In this example, the y-sensitivity is 2 V/cm so the d.c. voltage is 2 cm × 2 V/cm = 4V.

With the timebase ON (right) the line is seen.

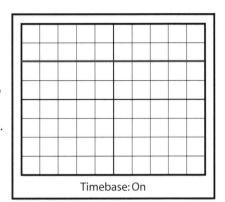

Timebase: On

Measurement of Time and Frequency

A CRO shows a graph of voltage against time, so it can be used measure the time interval between two events and gives us a method of measuring the frequency of an alternating voltage.

Worked Example

When an a.c. voltage is applied to a CRO, the waveform shown on the right is displayed with the CRO settings below:
- y-sensitivity = 4 V cm⁻¹
- timebase setting = 5 ms cm⁻¹

Each square on the screen is 1 cm. Find the frequency of the a.c. voltage.

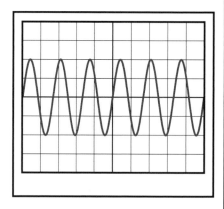

Six complete waves are shown. The width of the screen = 10 cm.

So time shown on screen = 10 cm × 5 ms cm⁻¹ = 50 ms

The period T of one wave = $\frac{50}{6}$ = 8.33 ms = 8.33×10⁻³ s

Frequency = $\frac{1}{\text{period}} = \frac{1}{8.33 \times 10^{-3}}$ = 120 Hz

Note that the y-sensitivity is irrelevant when answering this question.

5.7 Particle Accelerators

Students should be able to:

5.7.1 Describe the basic principles of operation of a linear accelerator, cyclotron and synchrotron;

5.7.2 Compare and contrast the three types of accelerator;

5.7.3 Understand the concept of antimatter and that it can be produced and observed using high energy particle accelerators;

5.7.4 Describe the process of annihilation in terms of photon emission and conservation of energy and momentum;

Particle accelerators accelerate subatomic particles to speeds almost equal to the speed of light, and then crash them into one another to see what happens.

Einstein showed that energy itself has mass (remember E = mc²), so that a moving object has a greater mass than an object at rest. The mass of an object that is at rest is known as its **rest** mass.

The primary purpose of an accelerator is to **not** to increase the velocity of particles, but to increase the energy of the particles. Once a particle is travelling at, say, 99% of the speed of light it is not going to increase its velocity very much, no matter how much more energy is supplied. However, its mass increases as it gains energy.

For example, when the speed of a particle increases from 0.99c to 0.999c the mass increases by a factor of 3. The velocity increase is about 1% but the mass increase is nearer 300%.

Linear Accelerator (LINAC)

High energies can be achieved by accelerating particles in a number of steps using lower voltages rather than supplying all the energy in one go. The linear accelerator is a series of metal cylinders, called drift tubes, arranged in a straight line.

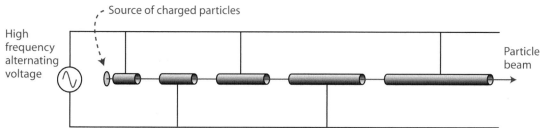

A **high frequency alternating voltage** is used to accelerate the charged particles in a series of steps until they reach very high energies. Using an alternating voltage rather than a direct voltage has the advantage that transformers can be used to produce high voltages for acceleration in each stage.

The electric field exists in the gaps **between** the drift tubes. When the charged particles arrive at this gap they are accelerated across the gap and gain kinetic energy. There is no electric field **inside** the metal drift tubes so the electrons are not accelerated here, but instead move with constant speed.

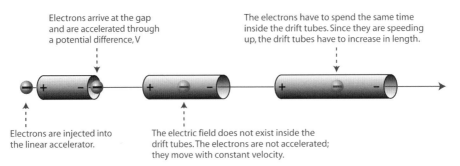

Electrons arrive at the gap and are accelerated through a potential difference, V

The electrons have to spend the same time inside the drift tubes. Since they are speeding up, the drift tubes have to increase in length.

Electrons are injected into the linear accelerator.

The electric field does not exist inside the drift tubes. The electrons are not accelerated; they move with constant velocity.

The drift tubes gradually become longer as the charged particles move down the linear accelerator. This increase in length ensures that the charged particles arrive at the gap between the electrodes at the correct time to receive maximum acceleration across the gap. Gaining energy in this way is known as synchronous acceleration.

The increase in energy as the charged particles are accelerated across the gap is **qV**, where q is the charge on the particle and V the maximum potential difference of the applied voltage. After being accelerated across N gaps the kinetic energy will be **NqV**. Linear accelerators provide particles with energies up to **100 GeV** (100×10^9 eV)

Advantages of the Linear Accelerator

- The particle beam has a small cross section area, this means Linacs produce high intensity particle beams. In other words a large number of particles per second per unit area.
- Linacs can be used to accelerate heavy ions to energies greater than those available in the cyclotron and synchrotron (see next section). These ring-type accelerators are limited by the strength of the magnetic fields required to make the ions move in a curved path.
- Linacs can produce a continuous stream of particles, whereas the synchrotron produces bursts of accelerated particles.
- Energy losses are small, so no synchrotron radiation (explained under Cyclotron, below) is emitted by the accelerated particles.
- This makes the linear accelerator more practical for the production of antimatter.
- The particles are accelerated in a straight line so magnets are not required to bend the particle beam. This reduces the cost of building a linear accelerator.

Disadvantages of the Linear Accelerator

- Linear accelerators can be very long when high energies are needed.
- The electrodes (drift tube) are used only once per acceleration.

The Cyclotron

When a charged particle moves with a velocity v at right angles to a magnetic field of flux density B it experiences a force at right angles to its velocity. Its path is then circular as shown in the diagram. This is the path of a positively charged particle in a magnetic field directed into the page. You can use Fleming's Left Hand Rule to verify this.

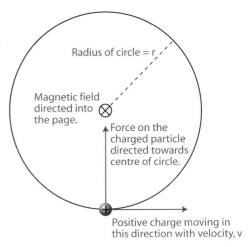

Radius of circle = r

Magnetic field directed into the page.

Force on the charged particle directed towards centre of circle.

Positive charge moving in this direction with velocity, v

The principle of the cyclotron involves the technique of synchronous acceleration but with an added magnetic field which results in the accelerating particles moving in a spiral path as they cross and re–cross the same gap between two electrodes.

The force on the charged particle due to the magnetic field is F = Bqv

This provides the centripedal force to make the particle move in a circle, so:

$$Bqv = \frac{mv^2}{r} \quad \text{or} \quad Bq = \frac{mv}{r} \quad \text{So} \quad r = \frac{mv}{Bq}$$

The time taken for the particle to complete one complete revolution is T, where:

$$T = \frac{2\pi r}{v} \quad \text{by substituting } r = \frac{mv}{Bq} \text{ we have:} \quad T = \frac{2\pi m}{Bq}$$

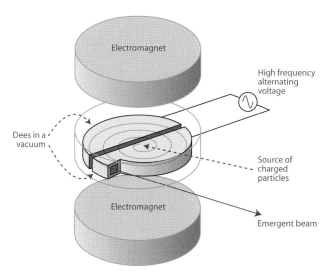

The above expression for T tells us that the period of the particle in the magnetic field is independent of both its velocity and the radius of its path. It depends only on the mass and charge of the particle and the value of the magnetic field flux density.

This is an important property of charged particles moving in a circular path in a magnetic field. It tells us that when the velocity of a particle is increased whilst the particle moves in a magnetic field, the radius of its orbit will increase but the time taken for one revolution will remain the same.

In a cyclotron, a uniform magnetic field is maintained in the gap between the two cylindrical poles of an electromagnet. In the gap, two hollow D–shaped electrodes, known as **dees**, are arranged inside a highly evacuated box as shown in the diagram.

The lines of magnetic flux act at right angles to the dees. An alternating potential difference is maintained between the dees so that an alternating electric field is set up in the gap between them. At the same time, the region inside the dees is free of electric fields and so the particles do not experience an electric force when inside the dees, as was the case for charged particles inside the drift tubes of the linear accelerator.

The diagram below illustrates how synchronous acceleration is achieved in the cyclotron. Synchronous acceleration is achieved when the alternating voltage applied to the dees executes exactly one half–cycle in the time taken for the particle to travel through half a revolution. This requires the period of the alternating voltage to equal the period of one complete orbit of the particle. Thus, if **f** is the frequency of the alternating voltage, the condition for synchronous acceleration is:

$$f = \frac{1}{T} = \frac{qB}{2\pi m}$$

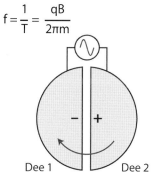

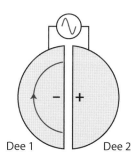

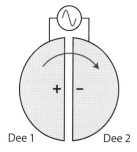

| The positive ions are accelerated across the gap from dee 2 to dee 1. | During the time when dee 2 is positive the positive ions move inside dee 1 with constant speed. The time spent inside dee 1 equals the period of the a.c. voltage. | The positive ions are accelerated across the gap from dee 1 to dee 2 . |

As the charged particle gains energy at each successive crossing of the gap, the radius of its path in the magnetic field increases. The maximum energy which can be obtained depends on the radius available in the magnetic field and the maximum value of the field which can be achieved. When the beam of particles reaches the largest radius possible in the machine, it is extracted from the accelerator by a deflecting electrode so that they leave the machine before striking the target under investigation.

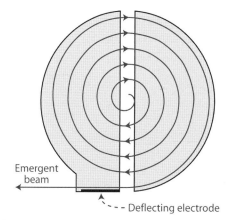

Advantages of the Cyclotron

- Cyclotrons are more compact than linear accelerators.
- The electrodes are used repeatedly to accelerate the particles.
- The Cyclotron produces a stream of particles as opposed to the bursts produced by the synchrotron.

Disadvantages of the Cyclotron

- The relativistic increase in the mass causes the frequency of the accelerating voltage and the time the particles spend inside the dees to become out of step. This limits the maximum energy of the accelerated particles. One way to avoid this is to use an enormous voltage so that large energies are reached in just a few orbits.
- Energy is lost due to synchrotron radiation. Synchrotron radiation is the name given to the electromagnetic radiation which occurs when charged particles are accelerated in a curved path or orbit.

The Synchrotron

To overcome the problems associated with the cyclotron a more effective approach is to change the accelerating frequency. A machine designed to do this is the synchrotron.

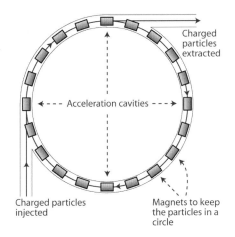

The synchrotron is similar to the cyclotron in that it accelerates particles in a circle. In the synchrotron, particles are accelerated and held in a circle of fixed radius by means of a magnetic field, the strength of which is varied to ensure that the particles follow a circular path.

As the particles accelerate the magnetic field is increased to keep them on the same orbit. The particles take less and less time to complete their orbit so the frequency of the accelerating alternating voltage must increase as well. The magnets perform two functions in the synchrotron – they bend the beam into a circular path and focus it to keep as many particles as possible on the ideal orbit.

Effective focusing of particle beams is very important as it:

*   increases the beam intensity, i.e. more particles per unit area per second
*   reduces the area of cross section of the particle beam, so that smaller evacuated beam tubes and smaller gaps between magnetic poles can be used.

Several accelerating cavities are positioned around the ring. These contain the alternating electric fields synchronised with the beam's orbital period and accelerate the charges as they reach and pass through each cavity.

Advantages of the Synchrotron

*   Particles can be extracted at various points along the path allowing a number of different experiments to be carried out.
*   The energy losses due to synchrotron radiation are reduced since the charged particles move in a circle of much greater radius than the cyclotron.

Disadvantages of the Synchrotron

*   Although the effect is less than in the Cyclotron, the accelerated particles still lose energy by emitting electromagnetic radiation (synchrotron radiation) when they move in a circle.
*   Cost is a major concern when building large accelerators.

Exercise 18

1. A synchrotron is a type of particle accelerator in which the kinetic energy of a charged particle is progressively increased as the particle moves around a circular track. The diagram shows the main components in this type of particle accelerator.

    (a) Explain why there must be a vacuum in the beam pipe.

    (b) State the function of the electrodes connected to high frequency alternating voltage.

    (c) Protons are introduced to a synchrotron of diameter 12 km from a linear accelerator. The synchrotron increases the energy of the protons until they are moving at 98% the speed of light. However, when moving at this speed the protons have an effective mass that is 5 times larger than that given in the data sheet. Calculate the required magnetic flux density of the dipole magnets needed at this proton speed.

    (CCEA AY221 Summer 2011 modified)

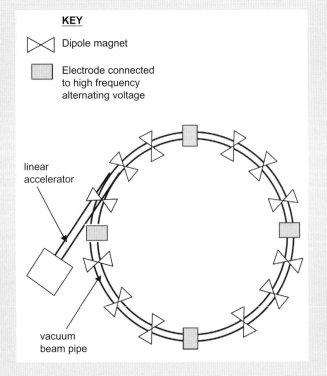

2. Particle accelerators are used to investigate the structure of matter. They increase the speed of particles which are then made to collide with a suitable target particle. The diagram below illustrates the main features of a linear accelerator (linac). In this linac an electron beam enters tube A and travels through the four tubular electrodes shown. Alternate electrodes are connected to the same terminal of the a.c. supply.

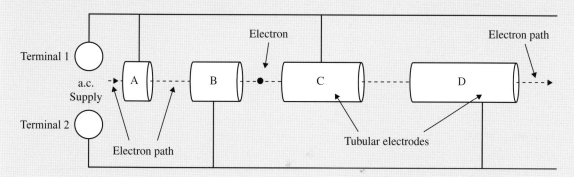

(a) State the polarity of the terminals (the circles) of the a.c. supply at the instant with the electron at the position shown between tube B and tube C.

(b) Explain why you have indicated the polarity in this way.

(c) Why is it necessary for the length of the tubular electrodes to increase?

(d) What is the change in electron kinetic energy, in joules, in the time it takes for an electron leaving A to emerge from D? The a.c. supply to the electrodes is maintained at 200 kV.

(CCEA A2Y31 Summer 2009 legacy modified)

Antiparticles and Antimatter

Every particle has an associated antiparticle with the same mass and in some cases opposite electric charge. For example, the antiparticle of the electron is the positively charged antielectron, or positron. The antiparticle of the proton has the same mass as the proton but has a negative charge. In a few cases a particle is its own antiparticle.

Particle–antiparticle pairs can annihilate each other, producing photons. Since the charges of the particle and antiparticle are opposite, charge is conserved. The antielectrons produced in natural radioactivity meet electrons resulting in annihilation and producing pairs of gamma rays.

When a positron ($^{0}_{1}e$) and an electron ($^{0}_{-1}e$) meet they annihilate each other. Their energy is converted to two gamma ray photons. **Two gamma ray photons are emitted in opposite directions so that momentum is conserved.**

The energy released is obtained from Einstein's mass–energy equation $E = \Delta mc^2$

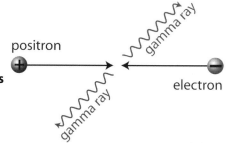

Mass of electron + positron = $2 \times 9.1 \times 10^{-31}$ kg

$E = 2 \times 9.1 \times 10^{-31} \times (3 \times 10^8) = 1.64 \times 10^{-13}$ J = 1.022 MeV

Each gamma ray photon has an energy of just over 0.51 MeV or 0.82×10^{-13} J.

Using the Planck relationship $E = hf$ or $E = \dfrac{hc}{\lambda}$ gives a frequency of 1.23×10^{20} Hz or a wavelength of 2.44×10^{-12} m.

Antimatter is composed of antiparticles in the same way that normal matter is composed of particles. An antiproton and a positron can form an antihydrogen atom, which has almost exactly the same properties as a hydrogen atom. Antimatter in very short-lived. Antihydrogen atoms survive for only 40 billionths of a second (4×10^{-11} s) before annihilation with ordinary matter takes place. Ordinary matter is the dominant type of matter in the Universe.

Exercise 19

1. In the film "Angels and Demons" 0.125 g of antimatter is stolen from the particle accelerator complex CERN.
   (a) What is antimatter?
   (b) Calculate the energy that would be released in the annihilation of this quantity of antimatter.

(CCEA AY221 Summer 2011 modified)

2. The annihilation of a positron occurs when it meets an electron. This is represented by the equation:
$$^0_1e + {}^0_{-1}e = 2\gamma$$ where γ is a photon.
   (a) Explain why two photons are produced.
   (b) Calculate the energy E of each photon produced.

(CCEA AY221 Summer 2010 modified)

3. The Low Energy Antiproton Ring (LEAR) accelerator at CERN is able to produce anti-hydrogen atoms. The diagrams are simple representations of normal hydrogen and anti-hydrogen.

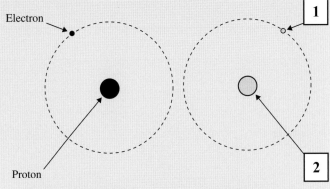

(a) Name the particles numbered in the diagram of anti-hydrogen.
(b) State one difference and one similarity between each corresponding pair of particles that make up the atoms shown in the diagrams.

(CCEA A2Y31 Summer 2009 modified)

5.8 Fundamental Particles

Students should be able to:

5.8.1 Explain the concept of a fundamental particle;

5.8.2 Identify the four fundamental forces and their associated exchange particles;

5.8.3 Classify particles as gauge bosons, leptons and hadrons (mesons and baryons);

5.8.4 State examples of each class of particle;

5.8.5 Describe the structure of hadrons in terms of quarks;

5.8.6 Understand the concept of conservation of charge, lepton number and baryon number;

5.8.7 Describe β-decay in terms of the basic quark model.

Fundamental Particles

An elementary particle, or fundamental particle, is a particle not known to be made up of smaller particles. A fundamental particle has no substructure: it is one of the basic building blocks of the universe from which all other particles are made.

Fundamental Forces of Nature

- **Gravity** affects particles with mass. It is very weak, and is only noticeable when large masses are present. Gravity is always attractive and has an infinite range. Gravity is the force that determines the structure of large scale matter such as stars and galaxies.

- The **Electromagnetic force** affects particles with charge. It is much stronger than gravity and it also has an infinite range. Electromagnetic forces determine the structure of atoms as well as determining the properties of materials and the results of chemical processes.

- The **Strong Nuclear Force** exists between neutrons and protons in the nucleus. It is clearly strong enough to overcome the electrical repulsion of the protons. It is a very short range force and only exists when neutrons and protons are within a distance of around 10^{-15} m of each other. The strong nuclear force determines the structure of the nucleus.

- The **Weak Interaction** is the name given to the force that induces beta decay. Beta decay occurs when a neutron decays to a proton and creates an electron and antineutrino in the process. This nuclear event creates a particle, the antineutrino, that is not affected by the electromagnetic force or the strong nuclear force. The weak interaction is the short range force needed to explain this effect.

Classification of Particles

Particle accelerators allowed physicists to study the nucleus and the interactions of neutrons and protons that form it. Particle experiments study collisions of high energy particles produced by accelerators and sophisticated detectors surrounding the collision point are used to identify each of the many particles that may be produced in a single collision. Hundreds of different particles have been identified. These new particles have a wide range of properties. One classification of these particles that emerged from all the observations was:

- Hadrons
- Leptons
- Gauge Bosons (exchange particles)

Hadrons

These are particles that are affected by the strong interaction, ie this is the force that acts between neutrons and protons within the nucleus. As more hadrons were discovered they formed two sub–groups within the hadron family, baryons and mesons.

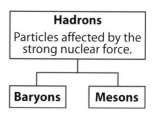

The **neutron** and **proton** are **baryons**. The proton has slightly less mass than the neutron. The neutron and proton are given baryon numbers of 1. Their antiparticles have a baryon number of –1.

Mesons have a mass less than the proton but greater than the electron. The pi–meson family consisting of two charged particles π^+, π^- and the neutral π^0 play a role in the strong nuclear force. The mesons have a baryon number of 0 as do their antiparticles, as they are not baryons. The baryon number B is a quantity that is conserved during interactions.

Leptons

Leptons are particles that are not affected by the strong interaction. Leptons are **fundamental** particles, ie they cannot be broken into smaller particles. There are three generations of leptons, the electron (e), the muon (μ), and the tau (τ) particle and their associated neutrinos. Each generation has a greater mass than the one before it. However only the electron and the neutrino occur in normal matter. Each lepton is given a lepton number of 1 and their antiparticles –1. The lepton number, L, is conserved during interactions.

Exchange Particles and the Fundamental Forces

The modern understanding of the four fundamental forces is that they can be treated as the exchange of particles. These exchange particles are the **gauge bosons**. Each fundamental force is attributed to the exchange of at least one gauge boson.

- **Photons** are the gauge bosons of the electromagnetic interaction, such as the repulsion between two electrons.
- The **W and Z bosons** are the exchange particles of the weak interaction which governs beta decay.
- **Gluons** play a role in the strong interaction, i.e. the force that exists between neutrons and protons.
- **Gravitons** are believed to play a similar role in gravity. However the graviton, unlike the other exchange particles, has yet to be detected.

The table below summarises the fundamental forces and their exchange particles.

Force	What it does	Strength (Comparative)	Range	Exchange particle (gauge boson)
Strong nuclear	Holds the nucleus together	1	1×10^{-15} ~ diameter of a nucleus	Gluons
Electromagnetic	Attractive and repulsive force between charged particles	~ 1/150	Infinite	Photon
Weak interaction	Induces beta decay	1×10^{-6}	1×10^{-18} m ~ diameter of a proton	W and Z bosons
Gravity	Attractive force between masses	~1×10^{-39}	Infinite	Graviton (by analogy only)

The Quark Model of the Hadrons

Neutrons, protons and mesons are made up of smaller particles, now known as **quarks**.

In the **quark model** the neutron and proton are made up of three quarks while the mesons are made up from just two quarks. The quark model has been confirmed by many observations from particle accelerator experiments. These reveal that there are six types of quarks. A free quark cannot exist: they are always combined in twos (mesons) or in threes (baryons). Antiquarks are the antimatter partners of quarks, they have the same masses as, but the opposite charge from, the corresponding quarks. When a quark meets an antiquark, they may annihilate.

Quarks have fractional electric charges such as $+\frac{2}{3}e$. There are six types, or flavours, of quark in total. These are shown in the table below.

Generation	Quark	Symbol	Charge Q	Baryon number B	Antiquark	Symbol	Charge Q	Baryon number B
1	up	u	$+\frac{2}{3}e$	$\frac{1}{3}$	anti-up	$\bar{u}$	$-\frac{2}{3}e$	$-\frac{1}{3}$
1	down	d	$-\frac{1}{3}e$	$\frac{1}{3}$	anti-down	$\bar{d}$	$+\frac{1}{3}e$	$-\frac{1}{3}$
2	strange	s	$-\frac{1}{3}e$	$\frac{1}{3}$	anti-strange	$\bar{s}$	$+\frac{1}{3}e$	$-\frac{1}{3}$
2	charm	c	$+\frac{2}{3}e$	$\frac{1}{3}$	anti-charm	$\bar{c}$	$-\frac{2}{3}e$	$-\frac{1}{3}$
3	top	t	$+\frac{2}{3}e$	$\frac{1}{3}$	anti-top	$\bar{t}$	$-\frac{2}{3}e$	$-\frac{1}{3}$
3	bottom	b	$-\frac{1}{3}e$	$\frac{1}{3}$	anti-bottom	$\bar{b}$	$-\frac{1}{3}e$	$-\frac{1}{3}$

Note carefully: for the purposes of examination only the up and down and their antiparticles are required.

In the quark model baryons (neutrons and protons) consist of three quarks, as shown below:

The **proton** consists of 2 up quarks and 1 down quark.

Quark	u	u	d

Charge $= \frac{2}{3}e + \frac{2}{3}e - \frac{1}{3}e = 1e$

Baryon Number $= \frac{1}{3} + \frac{1}{3} + \frac{1}{3} = 1$

The **neutron** consists of 2 down quarks and 1 up quark.

Quark	u	d	d

Charge $= \frac{2}{3}e + \left(-\frac{1}{3}e\right) + \left(-\frac{1}{3}e\right) = 0$

Baryon Number $= \frac{1}{3} + \frac{1}{3} + \frac{1}{3} = 1$

In the quark model mesons consist of two quarks, as shown below.

The **π⁰** meson consists of 1 up quark and 1 anti–up quark.

Quark	u	$\bar{u}$

Charge $= \frac{2}{3}e + \left(-\frac{2}{3}e\right) = 0$

Baryon Number $= \frac{1}{3} + \left(-\frac{1}{3}\right) = 0$

Beta Decay and the Quark Model

The weak interaction force induces beta decay. Inside the nucleus a neutron changes to a proton plus an electron (β^-) and an antineutrino. This process is given by the equation:

$$\prescript{1}{0}{n} \rightarrow \prescript{1}{1}{p} + \prescript{0}{-1}{e} + \prescript{0}{0}{\bar{v}}$$

In terms of the quarks that make up the neutrons, the process involves one of the down quarks that make up the neutron changing to an up quark. This process is given by the equation:

$$\prescript{\frac{1}{3}}{-\frac{1}{3}}{d} \rightarrow \prescript{\frac{1}{3}}{\frac{2}{3}}{u} + \prescript{0}{-1}{e} + \prescript{0}{0}{\bar{v}}$$

This is illustrated by the diagram on the right.

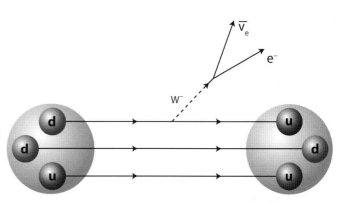

Exercise 20

1. (a) Pions and kaons are classified as mesons. What is the composition of a meson?

   (b) The equation $\prescript{1}{0}{n} \rightarrow \prescript{1}{1}{p} + \prescript{0}{-1}{e} + \bar{v}_e$ represents β^- decay.

   Copy and complete the table below with respect to the particles in this equation.

Particle	Name	Charge/C	Baryon Number	Lepton Number
n	neutron	0		
p	proton		+1	
e				+1
$\bar{v}_e$		0		

   (c) Which, if any, of the quantities charge, baryon number and lepton number must be conserved for any reaction to be possible? If none, write "none".

   (d) What is the quark structure for a proton?

   (e) Describe β^- decay in terms of quarks, include the intermediary stage of the virtual particle emitted in the process.

   (CCEA AY221 Summer 2011 modified)

2. (a) Some physicists consider the gauge bosons to be fundamental particles.

   (i) How do we define a fundamental particle?

   (ii) Give one example of a fundamental particle other than a gauge boson.

   (b) (i) Two electrons approaching each other do not collide, but exert forces on one another without coming into contact. Explain the role of the GAUGE BOSON in this interaction.

   (ii) Complete a table naming the four fundamental forces and the appropriate gauge boson for each of the fundamental forces.

   (c) (i) Name the two types of particle that are classified as hadrons.

   (ii) In what way are these hadrons different?

   (CCEA AY221 Summer 2010 modified)

Answers

Exercise 1 – Unit 4.1

1. (i) Momentum before collision $= (0.8 \times 0.4) + (0.6 \times -0.3) = 0.14$ Ns
   Momentum after collision = Momentum before collision
   $1.4 \times v = 0.14$, so $v = 0.1$ ms^{-1} to the right

(ii) The collision is inelastic because kinetic energy is not conserved.

Exercise 2 – Unit 4.2

1. (i) There must be a fixed mass of gas at constant temperature. So the complete statement should read: "The volume of a **fixed mass** of an ideal gas at **constant temperature** is inversely proportional to the pressure applied to it."

(ii) See text on the experiment to demonstrate Boyle's Law.

2. $\dfrac{p_1 V_1}{T_1} = \dfrac{p_2 V_2}{T_2}$ where: $p_1 = 280$ kPa, $p_2 = 310$ kPa, $T_1 = 15°C = 288$ K and $V_1 = V_2$ (so can be ignored).

Substituting: $\dfrac{280}{288} = \dfrac{310}{T_2}$ so: $T_2 = \dfrac{288 \times 310}{280} = 318.9$ K $= 45.9$ °C

Exercise 3 – Unit 4.2

1. Increase in volume $= \pi r^2 h = \pi \times 0.15^2 \times 12 = 0.85$ cm^3

From Charles' Law: $\dfrac{V_1}{T_1} = \dfrac{V_2}{T_2}$ so $\dfrac{40}{290} = \dfrac{40.85}{T_2}$ which gives $T_2 = \dfrac{40.85 \times 290}{40} = 296.16$ K $\approx 23.2°C$

2. The key things here are to note that the gradient of the graph (12 200 Pa m^3) is the product PV and to remember to convert the Celsius temperature to Kelvin. From the ideal gas equation: $PV = nRT$

So: $n = \dfrac{PV}{RT} = \dfrac{12\,200}{8.31 \times 277} = 5.30$ moles

Exercise 4 – Unit 4.3

1. (a) (i) The motorcyclist has an angular velocity because he is sweeping out an angle as he goes round the bend.
   (ii) 40 km hr^{-1} = 40 000 m in 3600 s = 11.11 ms^{-1}

   $\omega = \dfrac{v}{r} = \dfrac{11.11}{12} = 0.93$ rad s^{-1}

(b) (i) The velocity of the motorcyclist is changing as the direction of motion is changing. This means the motorcyclist is accelerating. A force is necessary to bring about this acceleration.
   (ii) The centripetal force is caused by friction between the tyres and the road.

(c) $F = \dfrac{mv^2}{r} = \dfrac{(260 + 90) \times (11.11)^2}{12} = 3600$ N

Exercise 5 - Unit 4.4

1. (a)(i) The mass–spring system (ii) The rotating cam

(b)(i) Vertical axis labeled amplitude. The curve should be a resonance curve for **lightly** damped system as shown in text.
   (ii) Immerse masses in water or attach a (light weight) lamina of large surface area (such as a paper cone) to the masses.
   (iii) Resonance curve should be for a heavily damped system as shown in text, including: reduced maximum amplitude, and a flatter peak displaced to a lower frequency.

(c) Since the cam interacts with the string twice in every rotation, the natural frequency of the system which has been forced to vibrate is $2 \times 16 = 32$ Hz.

Exercise 6 – Unit 4.5

1. (i) A is the mass number, representing the number of nucleons within the nucleus.
   (ii) Lithium–7 has 3 protons and 4 neutrons inside the nucleus.
   There are 3 electrons orbiting the nucleus.
   (iii) $r = r_0 A^{1/3} = 1.2 \times 7^{1/3} = 2.30$ fm.
   (iv) Mass of a lithium–7 nucleus $= 7.014$ u $= 7.014 \times 1.66 \times 10^{-27} = 1.164 \times 10^{-26}$ kg

   $$\text{Volume} = \frac{4\pi r^3}{3} = \frac{4\pi (2.30 \times 10^{-15})^3}{3} = 5.096 \times 10^{-44} \text{ m}^3$$

   $$\text{Density} = \frac{M}{V} = \frac{1.164 \times 10^{-26} \text{ kg}}{5.096 \times 10^{-44} \text{ m}^3} = 2.28 \times 10^{17} \approx 2.3 \times 10^{17} \text{ kg m}^{-3}$$

2. (a) Observation: Most α particles pass through the foil undeviated.
   Significance: Atom mostly empty space.

   Observation: Some α particles are backscattered.
   Significance: The positive charge and mass of the atom is concentrated (at its centre).

   (b) (i) $V = \dfrac{4\pi r^3}{3} = \dfrac{4\pi (r_0 A^{1/3})^3}{3} = \dfrac{4\pi (1.2 \times 10^{-15} \times 12^{1/3})^3}{3} = \dfrac{4\pi \times 12(1.2 \times 10^{-15})^3}{3} = 8.7 \times 10^{-44} \text{ m}^3$

   $M = 12 \times 1.66 \times 10^{-27} = 1.992 \times 10^{-26}$ kg

   $$\text{Density} = \frac{M}{V} = \frac{1.992 \times 10^{-26} \text{ kg}}{8.7 \times 10^{-44} \text{ m}^3} = 2.3 \times 10^{17} \text{ kg m}^{-3}$$

   (ii) 2.3×10^{17} kg m^{-3} (**nuclear** density is independent of A)

Exercise 7 – Unit 4.6

1. (i) $\lambda = \dfrac{\ln 2}{T_{1/2}} = \dfrac{0.693}{3.8 \times 24 \times 3600} = 2.11 \times 10^{-6}$ s^{-1}

   $N = \dfrac{A}{\lambda} = \dfrac{1.52 \times 10^{15}}{2.11 \times 10^{-6}} = 7.20 \times 10^{20}$ nuclei

   (ii) $N = N_0 e^{-\lambda t} = 7.20 \times 10^{20} \times e^{(-2.11 \times 10^{-6} \times 8.6 \times 24 \times 3600)} = 1.50 \times 10^{20}$ nuclei

2. Fill a polythene bottle with equal volumes of an acid solution of uranyl nitrate and pentyl ethanoate. The solutions are not miscible and the protactinium produced remains in the upper layer when the liquids have once more separated.

   Measure the background count rate while liquids are separating. The count rate of the protactinium is then recorded at 10 second intervals with a GM tube and ratemeter, and the background count rate is deducted to obtain the corrected count rate. Plot the natural log of the corrected count rate against time and draw the straight line of best fit. Measure the gradient of this graph: its value is $-\lambda$, where λ is the decay constant. Calculate the half–life, $T_{1/2}$, using the equation: $T_{1/2} = \dfrac{0.693}{\lambda}$.

   Safety: Observers should remain several metres away from the apparatus while the experiment is being carried out and the experimentalist should approach the apparatus only when measurements are actually being taken.

Exercise 8 – Unit 4.7

1. $E = Pt = IVt = 0.7 \times 4.2 \times (90 \times 60) = 15876$ J

   $$m = \frac{e}{c^2} = \frac{15876}{9 \times 10^{16}} = 1.764 \times 10^{-13} \text{ kg}$$

2. (i) Mass of LHS $= 235.04394 + 1.008665 = 236.052605$ u
   Mass of RHS $= 139.91728 + 92.92204 + (3 \times 1.008665) = 235.865315$ u
   Mass reduction $= 236.052605 - 235.865315 = 0.18729$ u $= 0.18729 \times 1.66 \times 10^{-27}$ kg
   $e = mc^2 = 0.18729 \times 1.66 \times 10^{-27} \times (3 \times 10^8)^2$ J $= 2.7981126 \times 10^{-11}$ J $\approx 2.798 \times 10^{-11}$ J
   (ii) E (from 1 kg uranium) $= (2.7981126 \times 10^{-11}) \div (235.04394 \times 1.66 \times 10^{-27}) = 7.18 \times 10^{13}$ J

Exercise 9 – Unit 4.8

(i) 1. The moderator slows fission neutrons down to thermal energy so that they are more likely to cause further fission in the nuclei of the uranium fuel. A suitable moderator fuel is graphite.

   2. The control rods absorb neutrons or control the rate of fission within the reactor. A suitable control rod material is boron steel.

(ii) The total amount of uranium in the rector core must be greater than the critical size so that the rate of neuron production is greater than the rate of neutron loss, thus allowing the chain reaction to continue.

(iii) The total amount of uranium in a fuel rod must be less than the critical size to prevent uncontrolled fission.

Exercise 10 – Unit 4.9

(a) (i) $_1^2H + _1^3H \rightarrow 2\,_2^4He + _0^1n + 17.6$ MeV

(ii) The fuels required are readily available: Tritium fuel is generated when lithium absorbs neutrons and deuterium is available from seawater; lithium can be obtained from chemicals in the earth's crust.

The D–T reaction is a one stage reaction with a large yield per fusion.

The fusion temperature is relatively low (compared to other fusion processes).

There is no long lived radioactive waste .

(b) (i) Charged plasma particles are confined to circulate in helical paths due to a powerful magnetic field produced by current–carrying field coils. The temperature of the plasma is increased by transformer heating action.

(ii) It is difficult to achieve a stable plasma at the very high temperatures required and to maintain it for a time which is long enough to achieve sustainable fusion.

Exercise 11 –Unit 5.2

1. (a) Attractive force between 2 point masses is directly proportional to the product of their masses and inversely proportional to square of their separation.

(b) (i) The radius of the space station's orbit is measured from the centre of the Earth so is $r_e + h$. Hence $F = \dfrac{Gm_sm_E}{(r_e + h)^2}$

(ii) $r = 6.4\times10^6 + 3.5\times10^5 = 6.75\times10^6$

The gravitational field strength $g = \dfrac{Gm_E}{r^2} = \dfrac{6.67\times10^{-11} \times 6.0\times10^{24}}{(6.75\times10^6)^2} = 8.8$ N kg^{-1}

(iii) Both astronaut and station experience centripetal force. Both accelerate towards centre of the earth with the same acceleration.

2. (a) A gravitational field is a region of space within which a mass will experience a force.

(b) Use $g = \dfrac{Gm_E}{r_e^2} = \dfrac{6.67\times10^{-11} \times m_E}{(6.37\times10^6)^2}$ giving $m_E = 5.97\times10^{24}$ kg

(c) (i) The period = 24 hour i.e. 86 400 seconds.

(ii) Use $F = mr\omega^2$ where:

ω = the angular velocity of the earth as it spins $= \dfrac{2\pi}{86400} = 7.27\times10^{-5}$ rad s^{-1}

r = radius of the orbit $= 3.58\times10^7 + 6.37\times10^6 = 4.22\times10^7$ m

$F = 2.11\times10^3 \times (4.22\times10^7)^2 \times (7.27\times10^{-5})^2 = 471$ N

(iii) Using $T^2 = \dfrac{4\pi^2r^3}{Gm_E} = \dfrac{4\pi^2(6.22\times10^7 + 6.37\times10^6)^3}{6.67\times10^{-11} \times 5.97\times10^{24}} = 3.20\times10^{10}$ s^2 So T = 2.07 days

3. (a) Attractive force between two point masses is directly proportional to the product of their masses and inversely proportional to square of their separation.

(b) The period $T = \dfrac{2\pi}{\omega}$ so $\omega = \dfrac{2\pi}{T}$ The centripetal force on the satellite $= mr\omega^2$

Gravitational attraction between the planet and the satellite provides this force.

$mr\omega^2 = \dfrac{GMm}{r^2}$ Substituting for ω gives: $\dfrac{m4\pi^2r}{T^2} = \dfrac{GMm}{r^2}$

This can be re–arranged to give $T^2 = \dfrac{4\pi^2r^3}{GM}$

(c) (i) A satellite in a geostationary orbit takes 24 hours to complete one orbit, the same time that the Earth takes to complete one rotation on its axis. Such a satellite remains directly over one point on the equator.

(ii) Substitution of values into this equation will give a value for the radius of the orbit.

$T^2 = \dfrac{4\pi^2r^3}{GM}$ so: $86400^2 = \dfrac{4\pi^2 \times r^3}{6.67\times10^{-11} \times 5.98\times10^{24}}$ giving: $r = 4.22\times10^7$ m

To obtain its height above the surface subtract the radius of the Earth.

Height $= 4.22\times10^7 - 6.37\times10^6 = 3.59\times10^7$ m

(iii) The linear velocity is given by $v = \omega r$.

The angular velocity $\omega = \dfrac{2\pi}{86400}$ and the radius of the orbit is that obtained in part (c) (ii).

$v = \omega r = \dfrac{2\pi}{86400} \times 4.22\times10^7 = 3069$ ms^{-1}.

Exercise 12 – Unit 5.3

1. (a) The force between two point charges is proportional to the product of the charges and inversely proportional to the square of their separation.

(b) (i)

Tension ↖
θ
→ Electrical attraction
↓ Weight = mg

(ii) $F = k\dfrac{q_1 q_2}{r^2} = \dfrac{8.99\times10^9 \times 5\times10^{-6} \times 3\times10^{-6}}{(0.08)^2} = 21$ N

(iii) $T \cos 30 = 21$ N therefore: $T = 21 \div \cos 30 = 24.4$ N

2. (a) (i) A field of force is a region of space within which objects with a particular property experience a force. For example a gravitational field exerts a force on a mass and an electric field exerts a force on a charged object.

(ii) See text on page 38.

(b) (i) $W = mg = 2.30\times10^{-3} \times 9.81 = 2.25\times10^{-2}$ N (remember to change g to kg)

(ii) Use $F = qE$ Since $E = \dfrac{V}{d}$, then $F = q\dfrac{V}{d}$

$= 3.40\times10^{-6} \times \dfrac{160}{0.09} = 6.04\times10^{-3}$ N

3. (a) The electric field due to Q_1 is to the right and that of Q_2 is to the left.
Remember both are positive charges so the electric field of each acts radially outwards.

$E_A = E_B$ therefore: $k\dfrac{q_1}{r_1^{\,2}} = k\dfrac{q_2}{r_2^{\,2}}$ The constant k can be eliminated.

So: $\dfrac{2\times10^{-6}}{x^2} = \dfrac{4.5\times10^{-6}}{(0.2-x)^2}$ which simplifies to $\dfrac{2}{4.5} = \dfrac{x^2}{(0.2-x)^2}$ giving $x = 0.08$ m

(b) The force on the charge placed at A is zero, since the resultant electric field strength at A is zero.

Exercise 13 – Unit 5.4

1. (a) The energy stored is given by $E = \frac{1}{2}CV^2$. The use of this for the two capacitors gives:
For the 2 µF capacitor we have $5.76\times10^{-4} = \frac{1}{2} \times 2\times10^{-6} \times V^2$ so $V = 24$ V
For the 8 µF capacitor we have $5.76\times10^{-4} = \frac{1}{2} \times 8\times10^{-6} \times V^2$ so $V = 12$ V

(b) (i) When the switch is closed the total charge remains the same: remember the conservation of charge met during AS module 1.

For a capacitor the energy stored is also given by $E = \dfrac{Q^2}{2C}$

For the 2 µF capacitor we have $5.76\times10^{-4} = \dfrac{Q^2}{2 \times 2\times10^{-6}}$ giving $Q = 4.8\times10^{-5}$ C

For the 8 mF capacitor we have $5.76\times10^{-4} = \dfrac{Q^2}{2 \times 8\times10^{-6}}$ giving $Q = 9.6\times10^{-5}$ C

When the switch is closed the capacitors are now connected in parallel.
The total capacitance is now 10µF and the total charge is 14.4×10^{-5} C
Using $Q = CV$ gives $V = 14.4$ V

(ii) Since the total charge on the capacitors remains constant electrons from the capacitor C_1 transfer to the capacitor C_2. This happens because C_1 is at a higher potential than C_2. The transfer stops when the potential difference across each capacitor become equal.

2. (a) (i) $E = \frac{1}{2}CV^2$

(ii)

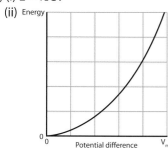

(iii) $Q = CV$ so $30\,\mu C = 10\,\mu F \times V$ so $V = 3\,V$

$90\,\mu C = 10\mu F \times V$ so $V = 9\,V$

Answer is the range 3 V to 9 V

(b) (i) $E = \dfrac{Q^2}{2C}$

(ii) Each has the same charge so the largest capacitor has the least energy, ie 9 µF.

3. (a)

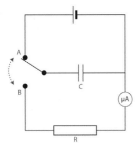

(b) See the method described in the text.

Exercise 14 – Unit 5.5

1. (a) (i) The force on the wire acts upwards.

(ii) The upward force on the wire may be treated as the action force then by Newton's Third Law there is an equal but opposite reaction force exerted on the magnet assembly.

(b) (i) The electronic scale reads a HIGHER value when the wire exerts a downwards force of equal magnitude on the magnet assembly (not on the scales). When the current direction is reversed then a LOWER reading is obtained because the wire then exerts an upward force on the magnet assembly.

(ii) Plot current/A on the x-axis and Reading 1/g on the y-axis. This produces a straight line passing through the origin. From the graph a current of 4.00 should give a scale reading of 1.02 g.

Convert this to newtons: $F = 1.02 \times 10^{-3} \times 9.81 = 0.01\,N$

(iii) $F = BIl$ so $0.01 = B \times 4.00 \times 0.12 = 0.48\,B$

So $B = 0.01 \div 0.48 = 0.021\,T$

Exercise 15 – Unit 5.5

1. (a) (i) Induced e.m.f. equals (or is proportional to) the rate of change of flux linkage.

(ii) Sketch showing: magnetic field, a conductor such as a coil, voltmeter or ammeter as shown below.

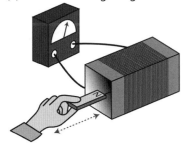

Text to explain how the change in flux linkage is achieved, ie by moving the magnet into and out of the coil. Then relate the change to the detector variation, ie the movement of the magnet relative to the coil induces an e.m.f in the coil as observed by a deflection of the meter. Finally, explain what is done to apparatus, ie: when the magnet is moved faster this creates a larger e.m.f. since the rate of change of flux linkage has increased; move the magnet slower and the induced e.m.f. is smaller because the rate of change of flux linkage is less.

(b) e.m.f. = rate of change of flux linkage

Flux linkage $N\Phi = BAN = 600 \times 10^{-6} \times 4.0 \times 10^{-3} \times 1 = 2.4 \times 10^{-6}\,Wb$

Rate of change of flux linkage $= 2.4 \times 10^{-6} \div 0.8 = 3 \times 10^{-6}\,V$

Current $I = \dfrac{V}{R} = \dfrac{3 \times 10^{-6}}{2.6} = 1.2 \times 10^{-6}\,A\ (1.2mA)$

2. The induced e.m.f. equals the rate of change of magnetic flux, or in this case the gradient of the graph. Lenz's Law introduced a negative sign into the calculation to indicate that induced e.m.f. opposes the change causing it. This means that the induced e.m.f. is the negative of the gradient of the flux graph shown. So we draw the graph:

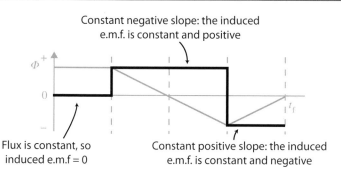

Constant negative slope: the induced
e.m.f. is constant and positive

Flux is constant, so
induced e.m.f = 0

Constant positive slope: the induced
e.m.f. is constant and negative

Exercise 16 – Unit 5.5

1. (a) Include the following points: Heat produced by eddy currents in the core is reduced by laminating the iron core. Magnetic flux leakage is reduced by a continuous core. Heat produced in wires reduced by selecting low resistance wire such as copper. Heat generated in core by continual magnetising and demagnetising is reduced by manufacturing the core from iron rather than steel.

(b) (i) $\dfrac{N_s}{N_p} = \dfrac{V_s}{V_p}$ so $\dfrac{2800}{500} = \dfrac{V_s}{230}$ giving $V_s = 1288$ V (1.29 kV)

(ii) e.m.f. = rate of change in flux linkage or equals $\dfrac{BAN}{t}$ or the flux change in 1 second.

So $1290 = \dfrac{B \times 2.20 \times 10^{-4} \times 2800}{t}$ where $t = 1$ s

So flux density change in 1 second = 2094 Ts^{-1}

2. (a) (i) Turn ratio $= \dfrac{N_s}{N_p} = \dfrac{V_s}{V_p} = \dfrac{240}{6} = 40$

(ii) If 100% efficient Power in = Power out

$I_p \times V_p = I_s \times V_s = 2.0$ W

Primary current $I_p = \dfrac{2.0}{240} = 8.33 \times 10^{-3}$ A (8.33 mA)

Secondary current $I_s = \dfrac{2.0}{6.0} = 0.333$ A (333 mA)

(b) (i) $I = \dfrac{P}{V}$

(ii) $P_{loss} = I^2 X = \dfrac{P^2 X}{V^2}$ Since P and X are constants, the power loss is proportional to $\dfrac{1}{V^2}$.

Exercise 17 – Unit 5.6

1. (a) (i) $E = \dfrac{V}{d} = \dfrac{148}{80 \times 10^{-3}} = 1.85 \times 10^3$ Vm^{-1}

(ii) $a = \dfrac{F}{m} = \dfrac{2.96 \times 10^{-16}}{1.66 \times 10^{-27}} = 1.77 \times 10^{11}$ ms^{-2}

(b) Horizontal velocity v_o remains constant $= 4.00 \times 10^5$ ms^{-1}

Time spent in the electric field = horizontal distance (120mm) divided by the constant horizontal velocity.

Time $= \dfrac{120 \times 10^{-3}}{4.00 \times 10^5} = 3.0 \times 10^{-7}$ s

Vertical velocity $= u + at = 0 + 1.77 \times 10^{11} \times 3.0 \times 10^{-7} = 5.31 \times 10^4$ ms^{-1}

The velocity on exiting the electric field is the resultant of these velocities. Using Pythagoras Theorem:

$v^2 = (4.00 \times 10^5)^2 + (5.31 \times 10^4)^2$ giving $v = 4.04 \times 10^5$ ms^{-1}

The angle θ to the horizontal is obtained by: $\tan \theta = \dfrac{5.31 \times 10^4}{4.00 \times 10^5}$ giving $\theta = 7.56°$.

This is below the horizontal since the protons are attracted downwards towards the negatively charged plate.

2. (a) (i) A charge moving in a magnetic field experiences a force. The force always acts at right angles to the velocity or path, hence the charges move in circular paths.

(ii) F = Bqv and provides the centripetal force. So by equating:

$Bqv = \dfrac{mv^2}{r}$ Dividing both sides by v gives: $Bq = \dfrac{mv}{r}$ Re–arranging gives: $r = \dfrac{mv}{Bq}$

(iii) $r = \dfrac{mv}{Bq} = \dfrac{6.6 \times 10^{-27} \times 1.55 \times 10^6}{0.80 \times 3.2 \times 10^{-19}} = 0.0399$ and to the nearest centimetre we have = 4.0 cm

(iv) Curved/circular path to right, and then straight as it leaves the magnetic field.

(b) (i) A curved path of smaller radius.

(ii) $r = \dfrac{mv}{Bq}$ So when B is doubled, the radius r is halved.

Exercise 18 – Unit 5.7

1. (a) To prevent energy losses through collisions between the protons and air molecules.

   (b) They accelerate the protons through a high voltage so giving them more energy.

   (c) The magnetic force is given by F = Bqv and this provides the centripetal force $= \dfrac{mv^2}{r}$

   $B = \dfrac{mv}{rq} = \dfrac{5 \times 1.67 \times 10^{-27} \times 0.98 \times 3.00 \times 10^8}{12000 \times 1.60 \times 10^{-19}} = 2.56 \times 10^{-3}$ T

2. (a) Bottom terminal NEGATIVE, top POSITIVE.

   (b) So that the electrons are repelled from the electrode B and attracted to the next one, C.

   (c) For synchronous acceleration the electron must spend the same time inside each drift tube. As the electrons move faster the length of the drift tubes increase to ensure this happens.

   (d) The electrons experience 3 accelerations each of 200 kV

   Energy change per acceleration = charge × potential difference = $1.60 \times 10^{-19} \times 200 \times 10^3 = 3.2 \times 10^{-14}$ J

   Since there are three accelerations, the total energy change = $3 \times 3.2 \times 10^{-14} = 9.6 \times 10^{-14}$ J

Exercise 19 – Unit 5.7

1. (a) Matter composed of anti–particles

   (b) $E = mc^2 = 0.125 \times 10^{-3} \times (3 \times 10^8)^2 = 2.25 \times 10^{13}$ J

2. (a) The two photons move off in opposite directions so that momentum is conserved. The momentum before the annihilation = momentum after the annihilation = 0.

   (b) Use the mass of one of the particles, ie 9.11×10^{-31} kg

   $E = mc^2 = 9.11 \times 10^{-31} \times (3 \times 10^8)^2 = 8.2 \times 10^{-14}$ J

3. (a) 1 = positron (or antielectron)   2 = anti–proton

   (b) Similarity: they have the same mass. Difference: they have opposite charge.

Exercise 20 – Unit 5.8

1. (a) A meson is composed of two quarks.

   (b)

Particle	Name	Charge/C	Baryon Number	Lepton Number
n	neutron	0	+ 1	0
p	proton	$+1.6 \times 10^{-19}$ C	+ 1	0
e	electron	-1.6×10^{-19} C	0	+ 1
$\overline{v}_e$	(electron) anti-neutrino	0	0	– 1

   (c) In any reaction all of the named quantities have to be conserved.

   (d) A proton is made up from 3 quarks: 2 up quarks and 1 down quark.

   (e) An up quark changes to a down quark and the W⁻ is the virtual particle is emitted.

2. (a) (i) One that cannot be subdivided into smaller particles.

   (ii) electron or the neutrino or the quark. A lepton is also an acceptable answer.

   (b) (i) A repulsive force between electrons is experienced due to the exchange of photons (the gauge boson for electromagnetic forces). The greater the force between the electrons the greater is the rate of exchange of the photons.

   (ii) Gravity – the graviton.   Electromagnetic force – the photon.

   Strong nuclear force – the gluon.   Weak interaction – W⁻, W⁺, Z⁰.

   (c) (i) Mesons and baryons.

   (ii) Mesons have a two quark structure, baryons a three quark structure.